MADAM&EVE's
Greatest Hits

by S. Francis, H. Dugmore & Rico

HAPPY 5th BIRTHDAY

Five Year Anniversary Special Edition

PENGUIN BOOKS

1

PENGUIN BOOKS

Published by the Penguin Group
27 Wrights Lane, London W8 5TZ, England
Viking Penguin, a division of Penguin Books USA Inc,
375 Hudson Street, New York, New York 10014, USA
Penguin Books Australia Ltd, Ringwood, Victoria, Australia
Penguin Books Canada Ltd, 10 Alcorn Avenue, Toronto, Ontario, Canada M4V 3B2
Penguin Books (NZ) Ltd, Cnr Rosedale and Airborne Roads, Albany, Auckland, New Zealand
Penguin Books South Africa (Pty) Ltd, 4 Pallinghurst Road, Parktown, South Africa 2193

Penguin Books South Africa (Pty) Ltd,
Registered Offices: 4 Pallinghurst Road, Parktown, South Africa 2193

First published by Penguin Books 1998

Copyright © S Francis, H Dugmore & R Schacherl 1998

ISBN 0 140 28241 6

Reproduction by The Rustica Press
Printed and bound by The Rustica Press, Ndabeni, Western Cape
D6802

Contents

Other Madam & Eve books

The Madam & Eve Collection (1993)
Free at Last (Penguin Books, 1994)
All Aboard for the Gravy Train (Penguin Books, 1995)
Somewhere over the Rainbow Nation (Penguin Books, 1996)
Jamen sort kaffe er pa mode nu, Madam! (Gyldendal, Denmark, 1995)
Jeg giver Mandela Skylden for det her! (Gyldendal, Denmark, 1996)

Madam & Eve appears regularly in

The Mail & Guardian, The Star, The Saturday Star,
The Eastern Province Herald, The Natal Mercury,
The Natal Witness, The Daily Dispatch, The Cape Times,
The Diamond Fields Advertiser, Die Volksblad,
The Pretoria News, City Press, The S.A. Times,
Fair Lady, Vodaworld, Flying Springbok and Student Life.
Ernie (Bladkompaniet A.S., Oslo) Larson! (Atlantic Forlags AB, Stockholm)

To contact Madam & Eve

POST: PO Box 94, WITS Post Office, 2050 South Africa
E-MAIL: hardug@iafrica.co.za
WORLD WIDE WEB: Visit Madam & Eve at the Electronic
Mail and Guardian's Web page: http://www.mg.co.za/mg/

Introduction

This book celebrates five years of Madam & Eve.

Over eighteen hundred cartoons, ten thousand sheets of drawing paper, 257 pen nibs, and over eight litres of India ink. Believe it or not, if you laid each cartoon we've ever done *end to end, starting at Durban,* they would reach ... well, we have no idea, because we're not going to do that. Suppose it starts raining and the paper gets soggy? Not to mention people passing by and helping themselves to a free Madam & Eve original cartoon just lying in the road. That's, of course, if the wind doesn't blow them away first.

But we digress. The reason for this book is simple: in the five years we've been writing and drawing Madam & Eve, we can't even walk down the street without complete strangers coming up to us and asking questions. Questions like 'Where do you guys get your ideas?' 'Which are your personal favourite cartoon strips?' and 'Where are your wallets — hand them over now or I'll shoot.' We get these questions all the time.

And that's why we decided finally to answer them — *and* at the same time celebrate Madam & Eve's first five years in print ... with a special collector's book, *Madam & Eve's Greatest Hits.* Why? Just for fun. The money we'll make, of course, has absolutely nothing to do with it.

Anway, no introduction is complete without a few thank you's, so here they come: we'd like to thank our families and friends, our editors, publishers and booksellers. But most of all we want to thank our readers. Especially those who have been with us from the beginning. We hope you continue to stay with us for a long time to come.

And — oh yes. Last, but not least, we'd like to thank two women who were also there from the very beginning, and are never far from our hearts and minds today.

Happy birthday, Gwen and Eve. Here's to the next five years and another eight litres of India ink!

Stephen Francis
Harry Dugmore
Rico Schacherl
June 1997

1 In the beginning

Probably the questions we're asked most of all are 'How did you come up with the idea for Madam & Eve, where did it all start, and how did three white guys — one an American — decide to write and draw a cartoon about two women from completely different backgrounds?'

Here's what happened. The three of us first met while working on a South African humour magazine called *Laughing Stock*. You may remember it. You may not. It was published in the late 1980s, and it folded after 13 issues. But the publishing company we worked for didn't fire us. In fact, we were promoted to the greeting card division. For the next year, we turned out hundreds of humorous greeting cards and 'gift' books. Books with strange but amusing titles like: *101 Uses For A Dead Yuppie, How to Make Love to Your Computer* and *Macho Pig* magazine. We also turned out others that we're trying not to remember.

Of course, it stands to reason that unless your name is *Hallmark*, any company with a greeting card division, or a company releasing publications with titles such as *The Barf Book* (we're not joking; that's one of the ones we're trying to forget) might struggle to make it to profitability. So we weren't completely shocked when the company was liquidated and we found ourselves out on the street with nothing but our last pay cheque and a box of unsold humour books. A decision was called for. Should the three of us all go our separate ways, or stick together and form our own ... well, company.

We decided to stick together.

All we needed was some kind of project that would not only bring in lots of money, but feature our collective talents: writing, illustrating and being funny. At first we thought about humorous skin tattoos with funny captions, but we soon realised there wasn't

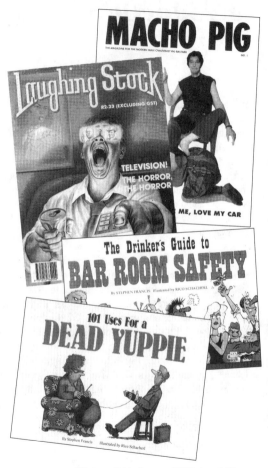

What we did before we did Madam & Eve ...
Hey, it was a living!

enough demand. And so we decided to create a cartoon strip. Something people could relate to: a cartoon about the South African way of life.

Amazingly, it was Stephen, the American among us, who came up with the best idea. Although Stephen had already been living in South Africa for several years, he had originally only come for a two-month visit; his South African wife had talked him into coming to see the country and meet his new extended family.

When he first arrived Stephen stayed in Alberton with his in-laws and noticed (to him, anyway) a strange South African phenomenon: the live-in maid. Sure, they have domestic workers in America, but nothing like here. In fact, when you call someone a 'madam' in America, it takes on a completely new meaning. Stephen observed the madam (his own mother-in-law) and the maid when they talked, laughed or argued, and immediately saw the potential humour in this relationship. Could this be the germ of an idea on which to base the new cartoon strip?

'Nah,' replied Harry and Rico.

Obviously they were joking — they thought it was a great idea. So work began on a new cartoon strip to be entitled 'Madams & Maids'. Luckily, though, Stephen came up with a much better title a few days later: 'Madam & Eve'.

The next step was finding a place to work. Rico, who was at that time renting a large blue house in Melville, volunteered the use of his lounge as an office. We had a phone, an old fax machine and a large table. The three of us would meet every morning and begin work on the cartoon. We tried different characters. We thought up situations. We exchanged punch-lines. We exchanged punches. And finally, when we had finished enough cartoons, we were ready to show them to an editor. *(Continued on page 10)*▶

One of our early attempts at a Madam & Eve cartoon which we promptly rejected. Madam was OK, but we weren't happy with Eve. She didn't have the sparkle in her eyes we were looking for.

In the first week of July 1992, the very first Madam & Eve cartoon made its début in *The Weekly Mail*. Madam and Eve looked very different in our early work, especially the lines on Eve's face to indicate her darker skin colour. This was before Rico discovered 'Letra-tone', an adhesive shading that is pressed down and then cut to the desired shape for various shades of grey. After the Government of National Unity was installed, our monthly 'Letra-tone' bill rose dramatically.

This is the very first Madam & Eve we ever drew, which appeared in the July 1992 issue of *Living* magazine. Now a collector's item, it currently hangs in freelance writer Gus Silber's house. We gave it to him as payment for the foreword he wrote for our first book. We were very stupid in those days and we'd love to get it back, no questions asked. If anyone's interested, we have his address. By the way, Gus doesn't have a security system.

We went first of all to a newspaper, *The Mail & Guardian* (at the time called *The Weekly Mail*).

'This is our new cartoon,' we said nervously, handing the editor a stack of Madam & Eve cartoon strips mounted on cardboard. 'You may have heard of us. We're the authors of ... *1O1 Uses For A Dead Yuppie*.'

The editor stared at us for a few seconds. He looked down at the cartoons as we sat across from him, waiting for a reaction. And then he did something which we hadn't expected at all. He laughed. We were outraged. How *dare* he laugh at us after all the hard work we had put into these cartoons!

And then we realised. He was laughing *at* the cartoons.

A few days later we went to see the editor of *Living* magazine. The same thing happened — he laughed.

Anyway, both *The Weekly Mail* and *Living* agreed to begin publishing Madam & Eve immediately. Naturally, we were thrilled — and promptly went out to celebrate. Halfway through our celebration, however, we remembered something important. Such was our elation, we'd forgotten to ask for money in return for the cartoons. And to this very day, five years later, we're still writing and drawing Madam & Eve for free.

OK, we're lying. But here's something that *is* true: we're still having just as much fun writing and drawing Madam & Eve today as we did when we first started five years ago.

A few months before we started Madam & Eve Rico was commissioned to draw the front cover of Two Tone magazine. The style he developed here played an important part in the creation of the eventual 'look' of Eve (see page 16). Even then, it's obvious that Rico had an obsession with large, round earrings. We don't know exactly what it means, but extensive therapy could probably help.

The second cartoon to appear in The Weekly Mail. The 'Is she available Tuesdays' joke is one that we used over again in different contexts in the years to come.

One of our earliest full-colour cartoons. We have no idea why we're reproducing it for this book, other than because it's silly and we really like it. Also, Harry enjoys dressing up in animal costumes in his spare time.

2   Creating the characters

When we first told our friends and family we were creating a cartoon strip about a South African madam and her maid, we weren't exactly bowled over by their enthusiasm.

'It's such a touchy subject.'
'It could be racist or in bad taste.'
'It's too realistic — do a cartoon featuring animals and cute kids.'

So we proceeded — but with caution. We knew from the beginning that if this strip was going to work, a great deal depended not only on the writing, but on the look of the characters and their personalities. Sure, they had to be funny. But they also had to be *likeable*. And when it comes to creating characters for a new cartoon strip ... you're hesitant. You're intimidated. Because once you decide on a character's 'look' and the cartoon is published, that's it. That character is carved in stone for as long as your strip lasts — with maybe a few minor changes.

So, with great trepidation, we picked up our chisels.

MADAM

For Madam, Rico drew a number of different sketches, many of which are, unfortunately, long gone. Finally, we decided on our basic Madam: pulled-up hair, huge earrings and a set of pearls across her neck. (After much discussion, we also decided to make her white.)

As you can see, Madam *did* change slightly over the first few months of publication. We don't think it was a conscious decision on our parts — maybe the character took on a life of her own — but she did seem to go on a diet and start paying a bit more attention to her hairstyle.

You'd think, however, that in all these years, she might have preferred to wear something other than a pink blouse.

Incidentally, readers always ask us if Madam and Eve are based on real people. The truth is, they're actually composites of people we know. The fact that Madam's first name is Gwen and Stephen's mother-in-law is also named Gwen is pure coincidence.

Of all the Madam & Eve characters, Madam has changed the most over the years.

Despite the subject matter of this strip, Madam is actually a great South African patriot. In all the strips we do, we hope to get across the fact that Madam and Eve are actually the best of friends. Although they'd deny it at every opportunity, we like to think that when the chips are down, there's nothing these two wouldn't do for one another.

15

EVE

We probably tried out more different versions of Eve than any of our other characters. Of course, we had already discussed Eve's personality: intelligent, satirical, witty and often sassy. Now all we needed was something visual to match. And so we stood over Rico, breathing down his neck. Then someone suggested that maybe he should actually be drawing first.

And so he picked up his pen ... We tried tall Eves, short Eves, thin Eves, large Eves, small Eves. But nothing seemed to click. They just weren't ... Eve.

The answer, it turned out, was right in front of our noses. Most artists decorate the walls of their work area with posters, paintings and photographs — and Rico was no different. On the wall beside his drawing board was the cover of a jazz magazine he had illustrated as a free-lance job several months previous-ly. We all stared at it — a cartoon of three women jazz singers (see page 10). The jazz singer on the left looked ... well, sassy.

Could this be what we were looking for? Using this image as a guide, Rico began drawing. We didn't even have to breathe down his neck. Five minutes later, we had Eve. And she's been with us ever since.

In case you don't know, Eve's full name is Eve Sisulu. Here's why we chose Sisulu: while we were deciding on what Eve's surname should be, we heard a true story. It concerned a madam who, after many years, still didn't know her maid's surname (see page 24).

We decided it could make a good cartoon and came up with a joke. When the madam asks, the maid indeed yells out her surname ... and the madam thinks she has sneezed, shouting back, 'Bless you'. In other words, for the joke to work, we needed a surname that could also sound like a sneeze. We had narrowed our choice down to 'Eve Achoo' or 'Eve Sisulu'. Luckily, we went with Sisulu, a venerable South African surname. And she's been Eve Sisulu ever since.

THE EVOLUTION OF EVE

We knew from the beginning that we wanted Eve to be smart and sassy and able to 'pull one over' Madam on occasion. Maybe if Madam paid her a little more each month, she wouldn't be forced to plot and scheme. But Eve's so good at it.

MOTHER ANDERSON

All novelists will tell you the same thing. Sometimes characters who are intended to be minor ones refuse to stay that way. They take on a life of their own, forcing the writer to keep bringing them back, chapter after chapter.

It's the same in a cartoon strip. After writing and drawing Madam & Eve for almost a year, we felt that we were losing some of the conflict. Madam, under Eve's constant satirical supervision, was definitely becoming more liberal. We decided to try out a new character, someone who was conservative and really set in their ways. Someone who could be oil to Eve's water. Chalk to her cheese.

Enter Mother Anderson, arriving from England to visit her daughter Gwen for the first time in years. And then she meets Eve. Although these initial strips were very funny, we finally sent Mother Anderson back to England.

B-I-G mistake. We got letters. We got phone calls. We had people saying 'That's *my* mother in your cartoon strip!

I love reading it — *and you sent her back to England?!'*

Naturally, as soon as we could, we brought Mother Anderson back for another visit. Over the months, her look has also changed slightly. Which is fine by us, because at least she's never left again. We hope she never does.

The original Mother Anderson (left) meets the Mother Anderson of today.

Is Mother Anderson completely and utterly conservative, set in her ways, patronising and condescending to people and cultures she's totally unfamiliar with? Nah — it just looks that way.

ERIC & LIZEKA

After the Madam & Eve cartoon strip started becoming popular, people began asking us probing questions about our characters. 'Was Madam ever married?' 'Was Eve ever married?' 'Do Madam or Eve have any children, and if so, where are they?' Naturally, we hated answering these questions. Because the truth was, we didn't know the answers. Even to this day we don't like to discuss this, in case we ever want to create a new character — say, Eve's ex-husband, who could just decide to return for a visit.

But we did decide to give Madam a son — away at university (which would explain why no one had seen him in the cartoon yet). And so, Eric was born. Which created more problems, because then there were more questions.
'What was he studying at school?'
'What are his interests?'
'Does he have a girlfriend?'

And then it hit us. They say that one of the truest tests for any 'liberal', whether black or white, is when their son or daughter

enters into a mixed race relationship (also known, in more politically correct language, as a 'non-racial' relationship). We began thinking how Madam would react ... and how Eve would react to Madam's reaction ... and then a whole host of creative possibilities began to present themselves.

We couldn't resist. First, we gave Eric Lizeka. And then we invited them over for dinner at Madam's house ...

HI. WHAT'S FOR DINNER?

The original Eric and Lizeka *(left)* meet their 1997 counterparts.

The more things change, the more things stay the same. Even in the new South Africa.

THANDI

We're big fans of the cartoon strip Calvin & Hobbes, and we thought it might be fun to try our hand at creating another character — this time one who wasn't a grownup. We came up with Thandi. Many of our readers believe she's Eve's daughter. In fact, when she was first created, she was introduced as 'Lizeka's little sister'. But for some reason Thandi took on a life of her own and didn't seem to want to spend that much time with her sister. Or even with Eve or Madam, for that matter.

Thandi seemed to want to hang out with Mother Anderson. And who were we to disappoint a cute six-year-old? We put them together and stood back. The chemistry was not only right, it bubbled over. Today we feel that these two characters together have contributed to some of our funniest and most poignant cartoon strips.

Part of the reason Thandi works so well is that, like six-year-olds everywhere, she calls things the way she sees them.

The early days

It's a South African reality: dogs with white owners seem to bark more at black people passing on the street, than at white people, and vice versa. Why? We're not sure. But we decided to do a cartoon about it — one of our first cartoons about racism in South Africa. By the way, note Madam's reference to 'Indian neighbours'. You'd think we would

have met them after five years! Maybe it's time to bring in some new characters.

All the cartoons in this chapter are from our first, now-out-of-print book, *The Madam & Eve Collection*.

'Wait till you hear this — it's perfect for a Madam & Eve cartoon!' We hear this all the time from family, friends and especially people we've just met. Sometimes we're able to take one of these stories and use it as a foundation for a new cartoon — and sometimes we're not. Here's one of the first 'true' stories we heard, that we turned into a cartoon: After working for her madam for almost seventeen years, a domestic worker suddenly quit her job, mysteriously leaving the very next day. Coincidentally, the maid's madam dis-covered that some of her jewellery was missing, and she called the police, who arrived and began taking down information from the distraught madam.

'What's your maid's name?'

'Mary,' offered the madam.

'What's her surname?'

'Uh ... Her surname? Uh ...'. She didn't know. After living together for seventeen years, the woman had never bothered to find out her employee's last name. Even the police were amazed. OK, you've read the story, now read the cartoon.

MADAM & Eve

BY S. FRANCIS, H. DUGMORE & RICO

SO... YOU'RE EVE'S NEW BOYFRIEND.

...WHILE I'M WAITING FOR EVE TO GET READY, DO YOU MIND IF I USE YOUR BATHROOM?

ER, OF COURSE.

UH, I THINK I CAN **FIND** IT BY MYSELF...

SURE THING... JUST GO **PAST** THE **TV** AND **VIDEO-MACHINE**...WHICH NO ONE IN THEIR RIGHT MIND WOULD WANT TO **STEAL** BECAUSE THEY'RE BOTH BROKEN!

...THEN TURN RIGHT AT ONE OF THE MANY **ARMED RESPONSE BUTTONS** CONVENIENTLY LOCATED THROUGHOUT THE HOUSE...

...THEN GO BY THE DOOR TO MY BEDROOM...WHERE I KEEP MY **WORTHLESS** IMITATION COSTUME JEWELLERY AND WHERE OUR **VICIOUS ROTTWEILER** SLEEPS...

© RAPID PHASE PRODUCTIONS 1992

HI. I'M READY... WHERE'S SOL?

HE'LL BE RIGHT BACK

...BY THE WAY...WHAT DOES YOUR BOYFRIEND DO FOR A **LIVING**..?

HE STEALS **TOILET SEATS.** WHY?

I JUST LOVE WORKING FOR SOMEONE SO GULLIBLE...

Early on, we decided that Eve should have a boyfriend. We named him Sol and introduced him to our readers — and to Madam, who wasn't exactly thrilled to have a strange black man walking around her house and using her bathroom. Although we used Sol again in other cartoon strips, he didn't turn into the major character we anticipated.

In fact, we get asked all the time 'Where are all the men — do Madam and Eve ever go out on dates?' Of course they do. It's just that they're very private about it, and we respect that. Hey — would you want your romantic life displayed in a cartoon?

MADAM & EVE

BY S. FRANCIS, H. DUGMORE & RICO.

MADAM, I'VE GOT TO TAKE A FEW DAYS LEAVE. MY UNCLE JOE JUST PASSED AWAY.

OH, I'M SORRY TO HEAR THAT. I FEEL BAD FOR YOUR UNCLE JOE...

...HE'S ALREADY DIED **THREE** TIMES!

WHAT?

I'VE GOT IT ALL RIGHT HERE. I'VE BEEN KEEPING TRACK OF ALL YOUR **"EMERGENCY LEAVE."**

ACCORDING TO THIS, YOUR "UNCLE JOE" PASSED AWAY IN **AUGUST '88,** IN **SEPTEMBER '90** AND **JULY OF THIS YEAR!**

AND LET'S NOT FORGET YOUR SISTER ...SHE FELL OFF A BUILDING **THREE** YEARS AGO, HAD A HEART ATTACK **TWO** YEARS AGO AND A BRAIN TUMOR LAST **OCTOBER.**

WELL, WHAT HAVE YOU GOT TO SAY FOR YOURSELF?

I THOUGHT SO.

THE DISHES ARE IN THE SINK.

DID YOU EVER THINK THAT IF I HAD A BIT MORE LEAVE, MY FAMILY WOULDN'T DIE OFF SO OFTEN?!

Knowing that their heartless madams will rarely give them a day off, maids are often forced to invent emergencies just to get some time off work. The trick is, however, always to keep track of what excuse you use. Especially if your employer keeps careful records.

Once, we overheard a conversation between two madams who were wondering what happens when they leave the house. Do their maids try on their clothes? Invite their friends over and have a party? Maybe even use the bathroom! These are obviously universal trade secrets that all domestic workers must take to their graves. We thought it might be fun if Madam tried to boldly go where no other white person had gone before — and bribe Eve to find out all these 'secrets'. By the way, since we've spent years researching maids and madams, we're some of the few people who do know all the secret things domestic workers do. If you want us to tell you, send ten bucks to: Domestic Secrets, c/o Madam & Eve, PO Box 94, Wits 2050.

It's always fun to fantasise. And it's especially fun to fantasise in a cartoon. This is the first cartoon strip where we changed the goalposts ... and let our imaginations run riot. We had so much fun doing it that over the years we've done all sorts of surreal strips using fantasies and dreams (see Chapter 17, Bouncing off the walls).

MADAM & Eve
BY S.FRANCIS, H.DUGMORE & RICO

ERIC...DO WE **REALLY** HAVE TO WATCH YOUR DOCUMENTARY FOR FILM SCHOOL?

TRUST ME, MOM... YOU'LL LOVE IT! AFTER ALL, **YOU TWO** ARE THE **STARS.**

I CALL IT "THE MADAM FROM HELL." WHAT DO YOU THINK?

I THINK YOU CAN KISS YOUR TRUST FUND GOOD BYE.

ERIC ANDERSON PRESENTS... THE MADAM FROM HELL — AN ERIC ANDERSON FILM

"..SOUTH AFRICA... LAND OF BEAUTY AND CONTRAST...."

"AND EVERY DAY A BATTLE RAGES... A BATTLE OF WILLS... BETWEEN AN UNDERPAID MAID....."

ERIC! GET THAT CAMERA OUT OF MY FACE!!

"..AND HER HEARTLESS, CRUEL MADAM..."

ERIC! FOR PETE'S SAKE! I'M TAKING A SHOWER!!

"WHILE EVE, THE LOWLY SERVANT, IS **EXPLOITED**..."

...ERIC!

"..THE MADAM RELAXES IN THE **LAP OF LUXURY** WITH FINE JEWELLERY AND CLOTHES...."

ERIC!! GET OUT OF HERE! I'M DRESSING!!

"WILL BLACK AND WHITE PEOPLE IN SOUTH AFRICA EVER RESOLVE THEIR DIFFERENCES AND LIVE TOGETHER IN HARMONY...?"

"..OR WILL THEY BE KILLED BY **GIANT FLESH-EATING DINOSAURS**?"

GIANT, FLESH-EATING DINOSAURS?

HEY—I THOUGHT IT NEEDED A TOUCH OF SPIELBERG.

We can't speak for other cartoons, but Madam & Eve didn't spring from our minds and pens fully formed. In other words, we didn't plan everything — we just kind of let the cartoon go where it felt right. One day, about six months after the strip began running in newspapers, we said: Hey — doesn't Madam have any children? And if so, where the heck have they been for the last six months? We decided to give Madam a son, Eric (named after Rico's younger brother) and have him away at university — thus explaining his long absence. This is one of Eric's first appearances — as a pesky drama school student returning home for the weekend to direct a student film project. (Incidentally, at the time this cartoon was first published, some of our readers may have been slightly confused — *Jurassic Park* wasn't even in production yet.)

It probably doesn't seem so important now, but at the time Madonna's book of photographs and sexual fantasies — which the South African censors promptly banned — caused a sensation. Never afraid of controversy, we came up with this cartoon, hoping to get the book unbanned. The fact that we wanted to see the book ourselves had absolutely nothing to do with it.

Apartheid aimed to keep South Africans physically apart. In this it largely succeeded, and to this day few whites have ever ventured into the distant 'townships' where most black South Africans live. The often mutual suspicion caused by this apart-ness might take a few generations to overcome. Anyway, looking back over the last five years, one of our great regrets is not doing more cartoons set in a township environment. Here's one that was.

For some reason, our readers really enjoyed these 'Madam Aerobics cartoon strips. Perhaps the idea of some madams going to exercise clubs, but having their maids do all the exercises struck a responsive chord. Or at the very least, pumped up their funny bones. At one point, we even considered using a line from these cartoons as the title of our very first book: 'She's not heavy — she's my madam'. We rejected this, however, finally deciding on the much wittier title, *The Madam & Eve Collection*. By the way, this cartoon features the first appearance of Madam's friend Marge, who went on to become a fairly regular character in the strip.

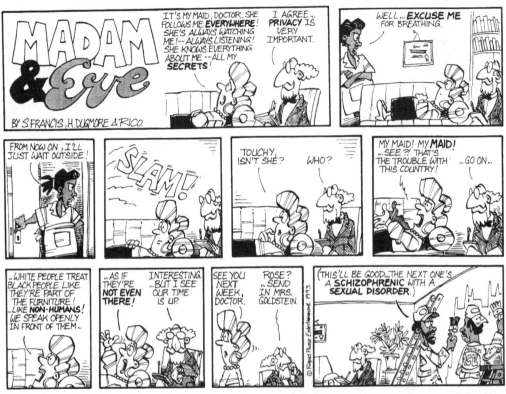

This cartoon was based on an observation Stephen made upon arriving in South Africa: 'I was amazed how families who employed domestic workers spoke so openly in front of them — as if they weren't even there. One night, during a family dinner, and a particularly candid conversation — I mentioned this and was told, "Ag, they're not interested in what we say and do. They don't even hear us." At that point — and I'm sure it wasn't my imagination — the maid serving dinner winked at me.' If we had to pick a top ten list of our all time favourite Madam & Eve cartoons, this one would definitely be included.

MADAM & Eve

BY S. FRANCIS, H. DUGMORE & RICO.

SEE MADAM? TAKING A **TAXI** ISN'T SO BAD! THEY DON'T DRIVE AS **RECKLESSLY** AS EVERYONE THINKS!

...MADAM?!

EVE—WHY IS THAT POLICEMAN ARRESTING OUR **DRIVER**?

...HE PROBABLY HAS A FEW OUTSTANDING TRAFFIC TICKETS.

HEY! WHAT ABOUT US PASSENGERS?! WE PAID OUR FARE!

TRY WALKING, LADY.

WALK?! ARE YOU CRAZY?! YOU EXPECT ME TO WALK?!

I JUST BOUGHT A NEW PAIR OF SHOES! DO YOU HAVE ANY IDEA HOW LONG IT TAKES TO BREAK IN ITALIAN LEATHER?!!

AND WHAT ABOUT MY SOAP OPERAS!? THANKS TO THE TRAFFIC DEPARTMENT, I'LL MISS "THE BOLD AND THE BEAUTIFUL!"

WELL!? ISN'T THERE ANYONE WHO'S GOING TO DO SOMETHING ABOUT THIS!?

(THE CRAZY WHITE WOMAN HAS A POINT.)

(IT'S TIME FOR ACTION!!)

"NOW IN IT'S 6th DAY, THE **TAXI STRIKE** CONTINUES, PARALYZING THE CITY..."

"POLICE ARE STILL SEARCHING FOR THE MYSTERIOUS MASTER-MIND BEHIND THE STRIKE..."

WILL THE "MASTERMIND" BE COMING OUT FROM UNDER THE BED SOON?

WHEN IT'S DARK. CLOSE THE CURTAINS.

Madam's very first trip in a taxi. At the time we did this, taxi drivers around the country were going on strike two or three times a week. We were told that when the taxi drivers saw this cartoon, they not only went on another strike, they also vowed that for the rest of their lives they would drive recklessly and always cut in front of other drivers — which, we're told, they still do today. So yes, it's all our fault.

HELLO? YES... I BOUGHT A **GUN** AND I'D LIKE TO SIGN UP FOR YOUR COURSE.

YES... FOR THE "MAKE MY DAY HOUSEWIVES' HANDGUN SCHOOL."

HOUSEWIVES' HANDGUN SCHOOL?

OH. YES – AND DOES YOUR INTRODUCTORY OFFER STILL STAND? GREAT! THANK YOU.

...INTRODUCTORY OFFER?

IF I ENROLL THIS WEEK I GET A FREE TOASTER AND A SET OF HOLLOW-POINT BULLETS.

©Rapid Phase Entertainment 1993 1-7

After the initial success of Madam & Eve in the *Weekly Mail*, we began negotiations with the editor of *The Star*, to publish Madam & Eve on a daily basis. This was, at the time, a really big step for us. Although we experimented with individual cartoons that were unrelated to each other, we soon discovered that Madam & Eve worked better when all five daily cartoons had a common subject or theme — a technique we still use to this day. These are the first such daily strips we ever did — with the unlikely theme of a Housewives Handgun School.

HI, I'M GWEN ANDERSON. I'M HERE FOR THE "HOUSEWIVES' HANDGUN SCHOOL."

UH-HUH... SEMI-AUTOMATIC OR REVOLVER?

REVOLVER.

ARMOUR PIERCING OR REGULAR?

REGULAR.

TURKEY OR HAM?

WHAT?!

YOU GET A COMPLIMENTARY LUNCH.

©Rapid Phase Entertainment 1993 1-8

PS: Five years later, we still love the granny flying backwards from the gun's 'kick'. Unfortunately, these cartoons are still relevant today.

MADAM & Eve

BY S. FRANCIS, H. DUGMORE & RICO.

HI EVE. HOW WAS THE MOVIE?

YO MADAM. IT REALLY GOT **DOWN**. I BE **CHILLED** TO THE BONE.

...A **SPIKE LEE** FILM, I TAKE IT.

GUESS WHAT, MADAM? I'VE DECIDED TO GIVE UP "DOMESTIC MAINTENANCE" AND BECOME A **RAP MUSIC STAR**.

YOU!? GIVE ME A BREAK.

MAYBE A LITTLE DEMONSTRATION WILL CONVINCE YOU. **WATCH THIS**--

♪ CHECK IT OUT— I'M HERE TO SAY— IT'S TOUGH TO WORK IN SUNNY S.A. ♪

♪ SO ALL YOU MAIDS— YOU GO ON LEAVE— Y'ALL CHILL OUT— I'M "RAPPIN' ICE— EVE"! ♪

...WELL?

A STAR IS BORN.

THAT'S **IT**?! DON'T YOU HAVE ANYTHING **CONSTRUCTIVE** TO SAY?!

...IF YOU DON'T DO THE **DISHES** AND WORK ALL **DAY**— AT THE END OF THE **MONTH** YOU'LL GET NO **PAY**.

©Rapid Phase Entertainment 1993

EVERYONE'S A CRITIC.

Rappin' Ice Eve. Luckily for us, her career as a rap singer never took off. Yo. Check it out, homeboy.

Remember Danie Du Toit, head of Telkom? Remember those horrible cloying TV adverts with Danie 'apologising' for Telkom's bad service to the sound of violins? Remember this cartoon?

To many madams, the maid's room is a strange and mysterious place. First, there might be the bed raised on bricks to keep away the 'tokoloshes' — at least that is what many white people believe (more on that subject later). Or, there can be bottles of sea water, brought back from the seaside by their friends and used for ... well, no madam actually knows what sea water's used for. With all these mysteries, we thought it would be fun to have a 'tour' of Eve's room — by a television crew — as if they were unearthing a hidden vault ... or the secrets of a Spanish galleon buried for hundreds of years. These cartoons have been reprinted around the world. We still like them, too.

Keeping track of 'permission to reprint Madam & Eve cartoons' forms is almost a full-time job for our office manager. We routinely get requests from companies, clubs, organisations and schools to reprint our cartoons in newsletters and publications. And, believe it or not, many teachers use Madam & Eve cartoons in final exams and tests. This particular cartoon seems to be great favourite with English teachers in particular. As they say in America — go figure.

By 1993 negotiations over the future of South Africa had been going on for months. Out of the blue, the far right wing organisation, the AWB, decided to gatecrash the party, ramming an armoured car through the front door of the World Trade Centre, where the negotiators were meeting. Amazingly, after the crash, they all got out of their vehicles and set up a 'braai', drinking beer all afternoon on the World Trade Centre lawn. What will they crash into next, we wondered? Which of course led to this cartoon. (The Doonesbury reference is to the famous cartoon strip Doonesbury, created by Gary Trudeau, which also runs in the *Mail & Guardian*.)

If you don't laugh, you cry

Throughout 1992 and 1993, random violence was a daily feature of South African life. Initially we didn't know how to respond to this violence in our cartoon. By its very tragic nature it was almost impossible to satirise in any way that we were comfortable with. But we did notice that ordinary South Africans were becoming desensitised to daily headlines about serious violence, and we thought that this would make a good subject for a cartoon. As it turns out, this is the only cartoon we've ever done that deals directly with political violence.

Like most South Africans, we were shattered by the death of Chris Hani, Secretary General of the SA Communist Party, and we wanted to do something in our cartoon strip. This cartoon expressed, we felt, both the deep sorrow and the growing unity of our emerging nation. It's also the first Madam & Eve cartoon not to feature any dialogue at all.

5 She who bears many children quickly

When Madam's only son, Eric, started dating Lizeka, we had a great opportunity to explore some of Madam's deep-seated prejudices. This non-racial relationship caused something of a sensation in Madam's household, and even today Madam is still recovering.

IT WAS NICE OF YOU TO ASK US FOR DINNER, MOM. YOU'RE HANDLING THIS VERY WELL.

NO PROBLEM! ...MY SON UNEXPECTEDLY BRINGS HOME HIS NEW BLACK GIRLFRIEND FROM UNIVERSITY... IT'S THE LEAST I COULD DO!!

Eric... She's eating her soup with a fork.

I know. ...Just keep smiling.

SO, HOW'D THE TWO OF YOU MEET?

ACTUALLY, IN JAIL.

WE WERE ARRESTED TOGETHER DURING A STUDENT PROTEST MARCH.

WOULD YOU EXCUSE ME? I HAVE TO CHECK ON THE REST OF THE FOOD.

EVE! YOU'VE GOT TO HELP ME! I CAN'T HANDLE THIS!

NONSENSE, MADAM. YOU'RE DOING FINE.

I'M A MESS! I DON'T KNOW WHAT TO DO! I DON'T KNOW WHAT TO SAY!

YOU CAN DO IT, MADAM! JUST GO OUT THERE AND MAKE SMALL TALK!

© Rapid Phase Entertainment 1993

SO.

ERIC... YOUR GIRLFRIEND HAS SUCH A PRETTY NAME. "LIZEKA" ...IT'S VERY UNIQUE.

I KNOW. IN ZULU IT MEANS... "SHE WHO BEARS MANY CHILDREN QUICKLY."

W--Water---

CHEW SLOWER, MOM.

MADAM & EVE

BY S. FRANCIS, H. DUGMORE & RICO.

47

Not only is this a funny cartoon, but we really love the way Rico makes Eric's hand "move" in the last panel. Stare at it for a few seconds, and you'll see what we mean.

We wanted to do a cartoon where Lizeka's parents also object to her non-racial relationship — to demonstrate that it's not only white people who can be prejudiced. We're fair like that.

50

Where's my gin & tonic?

The arrival of Mother Anderson was a real turning point for Madam & Eve. Over the first year of the strip, Madam had become a little more accommodating of both the New South Africa and of Eve. We felt the cartoon needed a new character — someone really conservative and set in their ways — who would be a perfect foil for Eve. We came up with Madam's mother from England, who would visit every now and then. What we didn't count on was Mother's instant popularity among our readers. After calls and letters, we realised we were on to a good thing and we decided to bring Mother Anderson back as soon as possible.

MOTHER, EVE -- I WANT YOU TWO TO GET TO KNOW EACH OTHER. YOU PROBABLY HAVE A **LOT** IN **COMMON.**

© Rapid Rase Entertainment - 1993

We had many discussions before sending out this cartoon to the newspapers. Would all the readers "get it" — or would they think that something had gone wrong and the dialogue balloons had fallen off the last three panels? We needn't have worried. The cartoon was so well received that we used the same device again in later cartoons.

SO. YOU'RE MY DAUGHTER'S MAID.

THAT'S RIGHT.

YOU'RE ALSO A BLACK PERSON.

THAT'S RIGHT.

I CARRY TRAVELLER CHEQUES. IF THEY'RE **LOST** OR **STOLEN**, THEY'RE EASILY TRACED.

© Rapid Rase Entertainment - 1993

GOOD! I'M **GLAD** YOU TWO ARE GETTING AQUAINTED.

"Hey, Bob! Come over here! This guy lives in South AFRICA! Hey, buddy. Do you have supermarkets there? Do you live in a jungle!?" Etc. Etc. Any South Africans who have travelled overseas can tell tales about these kinds of inane questions they're often asked by foreigners. That's what inspired this cartoon.

Stephen, being an American, was especially gullible when it came to South African facts and fiction. Before coming to Johannesburg, Stephen lived in New York City with his South African born wife Wendy. Wendy would frequently receive packages from home including large bags of biltong and, not wanting to share, she told Stephen it was 'dried snake meat'. Stephen fell for it hook, line and sinker, leaving Wendy to eat all her biltong herself. It took Stephen three years before he agreed to taste biltong for the first time, and another five years before his wife told him it was actually made from beef.

MY MOTHER CALLED YESTERDAY. SHE WANTS TO COME HERE AND WORK FOR THE MADAM & EVE PARTY.

YOUR MOTHER?!

CAN YOU BELIEVE IT? AS IF MY MOTHER WOULD COME ALL THE WAY FROM ENGLAND!

RIGHT! KNOWING HER, SHE'D PROBABLY WANT TO BE OUR CAMPAIGN MANAGER!

THE WINDS OF CHANGE ARE UPON US.

©Rapid Phase Entertainment - 1994

Mother Anderson's departure soon showed us how much of an important character she was in the strip. We and all our readers really missed her. The 1994 elections, and Madam and Eve's decision to run for office as the Madam & Eve Party gave us the perfect opportunity to bring Mother Anderson back. After that, she never left, simply moving in upstairs. Something just occurred to us, though — what about her house back in England? Who's living in it? Did she sell it? If anyone knows, could they drop us a line ....

MOTHER ANDERSON -- ALL THE WAY FROM ENGLAND! IT'S GOOD TO SEE YOU AGAIN!

MADAM TOLD ME YOU MIGHT SURPRISE US! YOU LOOK WONDERFUL! COME IN! COME IN!

©Rapid Phase Entertainment - 1994

DO I KNOW YOU?

We told you we'd used this joke again. The real question is: did Rico re-draw the last three panels or just photostat them? We'll never tell.

Mother Anderson's grasp of South African politics has always been shaky ...

EVE--THIS IS MOM'S TWIN SISTER VISITING FROM ENGLAND. SHE'LL BE STAYING WITH US A WHILE.

TWO OF THEM?! THERE'S **TWO** OF THEM NOW?!

BY THE WAY... THESE PEARLS ARE WORTHLESS. THEY'RE JUST COSTUME JEWELLERY.

EVE!! WHERE'RE YOU GOING?!   EMER-GENCY LEAVE.

Mother Anderson's twin sister arrived from England today for a long visit.

EVE! IT'S FIVE O'CLOCK!   ...WHERE'S OUR GIN & TONIC?!

By the time you read this, I will be dead.

With Mother Anderson proving to be a big hit with our readers, we thought 'Why not double the fun?' So we gave her a twin sister. That's part of the fun of being a cartoonist. You can invent anything. But Eve still hasn't forgiven us.

Surprisingly, in the entire five years we've been doing Madam & Eve, we could count on one hand the negative letters we've received. We have a deal with the SA Times (a weekly newspaper covering South African issues, distributed in the UK, Australia and other countries) whereby they reprint one Madam & Eve cartoon each week. They chose the 'All black people look alike' strip, unfortunately taking it out of the context of the other five strips in this particular series. Because of this, the premise of Mother Anderson's identical twin arriving in South Africa was also lost. We then received a hostile letter from London describing the strip as 'racist'. Usually we don't respond to letters, but in this case, we did, sending an explanation, and the 'all white people look alike' cartoon. The guy who complained realised how wrong he was and was so apologetic that he sent us flowers (OK, we made the last part up).

Although very popular, Mother Anderson's twin sister caused us to make a big mistake. Note how everyone refers to the twin as 'Aunt Edith'! Because they were twins we also got confused and began calling Mother Anderson 'Edith' in later strips. (Her name originally was Abigail.) Rather than change everything, Mother Anderson's first name is now officially Edith. So now ... her twin must be 'Abigail'. Damn. Now we're really confused.

MISTER PRESIDENT... YOUR STAFF ARE HERE TO SEE YOU.

GOOD. SEND THEM IN.

YOU WANTED TO SEE US, SIR?

YES! WHICH ONE OF YOU DREW THIS BIG **RED HEART** ON MY DESK BLOTTER?!

♪ THE PRESIDENT'S GOT A GIRLFRIEND! THE PRESIDENT'S GOT A GIRLFRIEND! ♪

CUT IT OUT, THABO.

AND IN OTHER NEWS, THE MYSTERY WOMAN IN PRESIDENT MANDELA'S LOVE LIFE HAS FINALLY BEEN REVEALED TO BE GRACA MACHEL.

WHAT?!

WHY, THAT TWO-TIMING LOTHARIO! HE'S BEEN SEEING SOMEONE BEHIND MY BACK!!

YOU DON'T THINK...

SHE HAS BEEN GOING OUT A LOT LATELY.

When the news leaked out that Nelson Mandela had a new romantic interest, we knew we had to use it in a cartoon. But how? Then we came up with the idea that Mother Anderson had a crush on the President and was insanely jealous ...

And speaking of the President, these original cartoons were actually presented by us to Nelson Mandela at the Foreign Press Association's annual dinner in November 1996. They're framed and hanging prominently in his office, or out in the passage, or in his lounge, or in his basement, or maybe the garage — hey, we know he's got them hanging up somewhere ...

7 Take us to your leader!

Trying to explain South Africa to illegal aliens is tough enough. Trying to explain South Africa to real aliens from outer space is almost impossible. But hopefully, at least it's funny. Readers seemed to enjoy these little space guys — that is why we occasionally bring them back to check on South Africa's progress.

Free at last!

Back in 1994 changes were happening in South Africa so rapidly that the ordinary citizen quickly seemed to get lost. It was hard enough just keeping track of all the acronyms, so we figured we should do a cartoon on that very subject, ASAP.

Because of her paltry wages, Eve often sets up little businesses to make some extra cash. Eve's booth, soon to become a regular feature of the cartoon, made its debut in this strip. A week before, negotiators at the World Trade Centre had finally set the date for South Africa's first democratic elections. We thought it would be fun to give some amusing predictions of how we thought the election — then still 18 months away — was going to work out.

71

MADAM...ARE YOU SAYING THAT MANDELA AND DE KLERK HAVE TO **SHARE** THE NOBEL PEACE PRIZE MONEY??

YES, EVE. ...BUT DON'T WORRY, IT'S STILL AN INCREDIBLE HONOUR.

OKAY. NOW THAT MR. DE KLERK AND HIS ATTORNEYS ARE HERE, LET'S GET DOWN TO BUSINESS, GENTLEMEN.

MR. MANDELA PROPOSES A **SIXTY-FORTY** SPLIT.

WHAT!?

THIS IS RIDICULOUS, COUNCILLOR. HOW DO YOU FIGURE MR. MANDELA GETS **SIXTY** PERCENT OF THE NOBEL PRIZE MONEY WHILE MR. DE KLERK GETS ONLY **FORTY**?!

SIMPLE. MR. MANDELA HAS BEEN ON **TWICE** AS MANY "NEWSWEEK" AND "TIME" COVERS.

ALSO, HE'S BEEN FEATURED IN BIG HOLLYWOOD MOVIES LIKE "SARAFINA" AND "MALCOLM X"!

HE HAS A POINT, SIR.

OKAY! SIXTY-FORTY! ...BUT I GET TO KEEP THE TROPHY!

When it was announced that the Nobel Peace Prize was awarded jointly to Nelson Mandela and F.W. De Klerk, our first thought was: How are they going to share the prize? Are they going to split the trophy in half? Does one guy get to keep it on odd-numbered days of the week? And how have been included in this book for another reason. Take a good look. Any ideas? We'll give you another ten seconds to think about it ... Still don't know? OK, we'll tell you — it's the first time in the cartoon's history that the Madam and Eve characters don't appear in their own cartoon. We still

We wanted to explore the reality that black and white South Africans very often had entirely different reactions to the coming of the 'New' South Africa. But then we realised we weren't explorers and we returned to the office to create this cartoon instead.

It's time to clean house.
The MADAM &Eve PARTY

Whatever you want, we promise to get it.

Gwen Anderson   Eve Sisulu

As the 1994 election date drew near, all sorts of fly-by-night parties emerged to contest the election. Organisations like the Soccer Party, the KISS Party and many others climbed on the election bandwagon — and made out like bandits, with election funding money handed out by the Independent Electoral Commission, the IEC. In this spirit, Madam and Eve also decided to form their own party to contest the election. We loved this idea — it gave us some great opportunities to send up the political process from the 'inside', and to satirise the wild promises that characterise politicians in election mode anywhere in the world. Imagine our surprise when graffiti artists starting daubing the slogan 'Madam & Eve for president' on walls in suburban Johannesburg. We didn't do it — honest!

Just before the first democratic election white South Africans started to get very paranoid — and the rumour-mill started working overtime. One popular urban legend suggested that if the ANC got into power, the re-distribution of wealth would include all white-owned houses. We couldn't resist coming up with this cartoon.

AND, IN OTHER NEWS, PRE-ELECTION HYSTERIA HAS GRIPPED THE COUNTRY. FEARING RIOTS AND DISRUPTION OF SERVICES, SOUTH AFRICANS ARE STOCKING UP ON TINNED GOODS AND CANDLES ...

... CAN YOU *BELIEVE* HOW *PARANOID* EVERYONE'S GETTING?

MOM! COME OUT HERE! YOU'VE GOT TO SEE THIS!

TWO HUNDRED AND ONE ... TWO HUNDRED AND TWO ...

MOM! YOU ARE NOT BUYING MORE TINS OF BEANS!

IT'S A MATTER OF SURVIVAL.

WHEN THE RIOTS START IN THIS COUNTRY, WE'LL BE ABLE TO BARRICADE OURSELVES IN THE BASEMENT, LIGHT CANDLES, AND EAT BEANS FOR THREE MONTHS.

IF THERE WAS EVER AN INCENTIVE FOR PEACE, THAT'S IT.

When you think about it, people with a healthy sense of humour usually have a sixth sense — a humour sense — that enables them to see the funny side of things. During the pre-election hysteria, many white South Africans began stock-piling goods in case they had to hole up in their basements during the riots and looting that were sure to take place in the post-election period. Supermarkets reported huge quantities of candles (for when the electricity supply was shut off) and tinned food (especially baked beans) disappearing off the shelves in the week before the election. Which is actually very funny when you think about it. Beans and candles? Barricading yourselves in a small, enclosed basement with lit candles, while eating lots of beans? We don't know about you but we'd rather take our chances outside — in the fresh air.

Although initially viewed by many South Africans with great apprehension, the 1994 elections turned out to be a celebration of the human spirit at its best. The South African miracle finally became tangible, with maids and madams standing in election queues for many hours, equal, at this level, for the very first time in South Africa's history. Easy to say now, but at the time no one knew exactly what to expect. Remember that yucky fluid South Africans had to dip their hands into when they voted? And the rumours that it could somehow reveal who you voted for, and that it wouldn't wash off for five years, until the next election?

The Independent Electoral Commission (IEC) had to organise an election in record time, as well as accommodate the last-minute decision of the Inkatha Freedom Party to contest the elections. Overall, the IEC did a heroic job in running the election, but they also made some classic blunders and infuriated almost everyone in the process. This cartoon expressed, we thought, all of South Africa's frustration with the long delays in getting the final voting tallies and election results announced.

Definitely one of our personal favourites. In fact, years after it appeared we still can't help ululating right in our chairs whenever we read it.

Some things change — and some things stay the same. This cartoon has been reprinted throughout the world, and we think it says it all. 'Free at Last' ... also happens to be the title of the second Madam & Eve book.

So whatever did happen to all those thousands of tins of stock-piled baked beans, and stored candles? It's one of the great mysteries of the New South Africa. If there's anyone out there who admits to stock-piling beans and candles in the pre-election period, please turn them over to the South African National Defence Force, Secret Weapons Division. They're a potentially dangerous combination.

We bet you thought Madam and Eve weren't invited to
Nelson Mandela's inauguration ...

Couldn't we just hum it?

The New South Africa had begun and suddenly everyone realised we needed a new flag and new national anthem. Remember the contests to see who could come up with the best flag design? We figured the least Madam and Eve could do was give it a try. We think they came pretty close.

COME ON, EVE! WE'VE GOT TO WRITE A NEW NATIONAL ANTHEM!

I'M TRYING, MADAM. THE LYRICS AREN'T EASY!

THINK SOUTH AFRICAN **IMAGES**, EVE! JUST LOOK OUT THE WINDOW! WARM YELLOW SUN! SKY BLUE WATERS! CASCADING MOUNTAINS! ROLLING HILLS...

...SKY BLUE WATERS...

YOU SAID THAT ALREADY...

MADAM -- WE'VE BEEN TRYING FOR **TWO DAYS** TO WRITE A NEW NATIONAL ANTHEM... AND WE ONLY HAVE **ONE** LINE...

OKAY. READ IT BACK TO ME.

"SOUTH AFRICA, WE THINK YOU'RE **LEKKER**..."

I'VE GOT IT! "...DISCOVERED BY THE FIRST GREAT **TREKKER!**"

THAT'S IT. I'M OUTTA HERE.

WAIT! WE'RE SO CLOSE!

We always noticed that during televised rugby test matches, when the national anthem is played, the South African team members begin to sing N'kosi Sikelel' iAfrika — and then desperately hope that the camera isn't on them after the first line. That gave us an idea — to have Eve make a little extra money by teaching whites the full verses of the national anthem. If you're white and you know all the words to N'kosi Sikelel' iAfrika, give yourself ten points. If you're a rugby player, give yourself twenty points.

When it was announced that the New South Africa would have eleven official languages, many whites began to feel guilty about not speaking a black language. This gave us an idea for Eve to have a little multi-lingual fun at Madam's expense.

We loved the idea of Eve hustling Mother Anderson into a game of poker. Then we noticed that all the picture cards in the deck were white people — and from there, the cartoon practically wrote itself. We've even toyed with the idea of actually publishing a special deck of New South Africa playing cards to sell in stores as Christmas gifts — Nelson Mandela as one of the kings — Thabo Mbeki as one of the Jacks, Winnie as one of the queens. Well, you get the idea. Although we thought it was a novel idea, we haven't done it — yet. Any playing card manufacturers out there reading this, give us a call!

Most kinds of humour have one thing in common: the element of surprise. Just when you think you know where the story's heading, someone yanks the carpet out from under your feet — and the sense of surprise makes you laugh. This is one of our favourites: it's cute, funny — and gets its point across ...

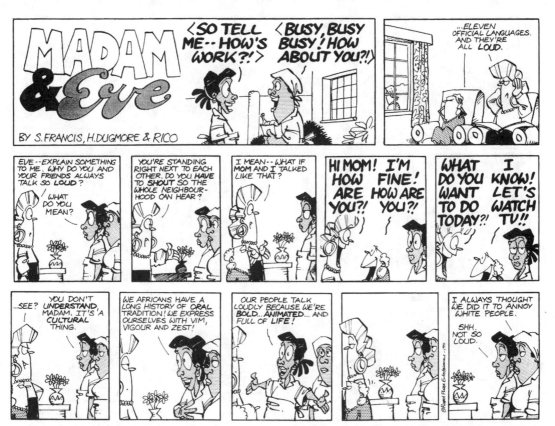

Who talks more loudly — white South Africans or black South Africans? And why? We think the government should spend millions of rands on a study to find out. In the meantime, just study this cartoon.

We love urban legends. They make the best cartoons. Here, one of the absurd rumours going around before the election was that everyone who voted for Nelson Mandela would receive a free luxury car in return for their loyalty and support. In a country of such stark contrasts of wealth and poverty, there is a great deal of poignancy to this cartoon, one of our all-time favourites.

10 The Mielie wars

Being an American and a 'foreigner' not yet used to the South African way of life, Stephen would often see or hear things that most of us take for granted. One day he walked into our office: 'I was trying to take a nap — and some lady kept disturbing me, walking down the street shouting "mielllllies!!" What's a mielie?' (They call it corn in the USA.) And so, the mielie lady was created ... As you can see, it took us a few cartoons before settling on a spelling for 'mielies'.

This cartoon was obviously inspired by one of our favourite cartoons, Gary Larson's The Far Side. By the way, when cartoonists steal from other cartoonists, it's not really stealing. It's called paying homage. And if you're still standing in a book store reading this, make sure you don't homage this book without paying for it.

The idea for this cartoon came pretty quickly. What took a long time was finding the correct Spanish lyrics to *The Macarena* and spelling them properly. It's amazing what you can find on the Internet if you know where to look.

'I vote for the thumb choice'

We've always believed that Madam and Eve's is no different from all employer/employee relationships. It all comes down to a simple algebraic equation: Madam wants to pay less, Eve wants to get paid more. This causes conflict.

Conflict is the first rule of comedy. Therefore, we have proved that all employer/employee relationships are inherently funny. This is why we all failed algebra.

NOT NOW, MOM. I'VE ALMOST GOT HER!

THEIR WAGE NEGOTIATIONS GET CRAZIER EVERY YEAR.

In this cartoon Madam and Eve give new meaning to the term 'grappling for solutions' in their annual wage negotiation. Actually, they've both been wrestling with their consciences. Next time they sit across from each other, they should come armed with a solution. Actually, they should stop trying to muscle in on one another's territory. (This is why we always try to avoid puns in our cartoons.)

WHAT ARE THESE SIGNS FOR?

IT'S THE LATEST THING. WE'RE GOING TO PICKET A MADAM WHO PAYS LOW WAGES.

GOOD, EVE! IT'S **ABOUT TIME** YOU MAIDS STOOD UP FOR YOUR RIGHTS! NEED A RIDE?

NO THANKS. WE'LL JUST BE STANDING IN YOUR FRONT YARD.

MY YARD?!

NOW HOLD ON JUST A DARN MINUTE!!

BETTER PAY! BETTER PAY!

Ever been tempted to exaggerate your past performance in order to get a new job? Go on, you can tell us. This cartoon was inspired by a situation at a major South African university where a new black deputy vice-chancellor was accused of embellishing his past achievements. Known locally as the 'Makgoba Affair', the controversy centred around whether the candidate, Professor Makgoba, had in fact done all the things he claimed he had on his CV. For weeks debate raged in the newspapers and on campus. Accusations of racism were levelled at both Makgoba's supporters and at the largely white academics who opposed his appointment. From our side, we couldn't resist looking up Eve's CV to see how she had originally got the job with Madam.

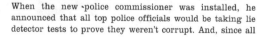

When the new police commissioner was installed, he announced that all top police officials would be taking lie detector tests to prove they weren't corrupt. And, since all Madams would undoubtedly love to get their own domestic workers hooked up to a lie detector — this series of cartoons practically wrote itself.

12 The Bill of Whites

Sales booths have a long pedigree in the history of cartoon strips. Lucy in Charles Schultz's Peanuts runs a roadside psychological service, and Johnny Hart's BC used endless variations on the booth joke. Even Bill Waterson's classic Calvin & Hobbes occasionally sees Calvin trying his hand at selling lemonade at the side of the road. We thought we too needed to take part in this rich cartoon tradition, so Eve, ever the entrepreneur, started up a range of ingenious mini-businesses, most of which are tailor-made to take advantage of Madam's gullibility.

We don't usually use puns in Madam & Eve, but occasionally something silly works. For some readers this cartoon became an all-time favourite, capturing the ambivalence of many white South Africans towards the new constitution.

13 T'was the night before Christmas

Somehow a tradition began: each year we'd do a special colour Madam & Eve cartoon to celebrate the Christmas season, usually published on the front page of the *Mail & Guardian*. Although we're including most of these cartoons in the next few pages, our first Christmas cartoon — where Father Christmas is unable to bypass all the security systems to deliver his presents — is still our favourite. It is reproduced here in the original black and white, since we only began using colour the following year ...

MADAM & EVE

BY S. FRANCIS, H. DUGMORE & RICO

'TWAS THE NIGHT BEFORE CHRISTMAS AND AT THE NORTH POLE, FATHER CHRISTMAS WAS READY TO ROCK AND TO ROLL.

HE CHECKED HIS EQUIPMENT, HE CHECKED OUT HIS SLEIGH; FOR SOON HE'D ARRIVE ON THE STREETS OF SA.

HE GOT SUITED UP. HE WAS UP FOR THE TEST.

AND IN CAME HIS ELVES WITH HIS BULLET-PROOF VEST.

HE'D BEEN THERE BEFORE... AND HE KNEW IT WAS VIOLENT.

...HE WAS HOPING HOWEVER, THAT TONIGHT WOULD BE SILENT.

HE REACHED THE FIRST TOWN AND LOOKED AT THE MAP. THE STREETS WERE ALL QUIET... COULD THIS BE A **TRAP**?!!

COVER ME. I'M GOING IN!

AND A MADAM AND MAID THEN HEARD SUCH A CLATTER... THEY AROSE FROM THEIR BEDS TO SEE WHAT WAS THE MATTER.

STANDARD FORMATION! MOVE! MOVE!

IS **THIS** WHAT IT'S COME TO?" EVE SAID WITH A GROAN. "FATHER CHRISTMAS DECKED OUT LIKE SYLVESTER STALLONE?!"

"YOU'RE RIGHT", SIGHED FC, "I GOT CARRIED AWAY. I EVEN PUT GUARD BARS ON TOP OF MY SLEIGH!"

"CHRISTMAS IS **JOYFUL** – WHY, THAT IS THE ESSENCE! SHOULD I BE **AFRAID** TO DELIVER MY PRESENTS?!"

"BOYS – DROP YOUR WEAPONS! THROW DOWN YOUR ROUNDS!

...AND LITTLE ELF UZIS FELL TO THE GROUND.

AND THEY HEARD HIM EXCLAIM AS HE DROVE OUT OF SIGHT-- "PEACE ON EARTH TO YOU ALL! MERRY CHRISTMAS, GOOD NIGHT!"

MADAM & Eve

THE TWELVE DAYS OF CHRISTMAS

BY S. FRANCIS, H. DUGMORE & RICO

ON THE TWELFTH DAY OF CHRISTMAS, MY TRUE LOVE GAVE TO ME... TWELVE SINGERS PRAISING...

ELEVEN CELL PHONES RINGING...

TEN WORKERS STRIKING...

MORE PAY — ON STRIKE — BET WAG

NINE SQUATTERS SQUATTING...

EIGHT MADAMS SHOPPING...

SEVEN MAIDS A-CLEANING...

SIX CRATES OF BEANS AND CANDLES...

CANDLES

FIVE GOLD-EN HANDSHAKES!

FOUR PARKTOWN PRAWNS...

THREE FRENCH INVESTORS...

TWO TONS OF SILVERWARE...

SPOONS — DESSERT BACKS — SUGAR BOWL — GRAVY BOATS — KNIVES

AND A FREE HOUSE TO GIVE TO WIN-NIE!

SOLD

MERRY CHRISTMAS!

Madam & Eve

110

MADAM & EVE

BY S. FRANCIS, H. DUGMORE & RICO

TWAS THE NIGHT BEFORE CHRISTMAS, AND AT THE NORTH POLE, A **VISITOR** PITCHED FROM OUT OF THE COLD.

"I'M HERE FROM "SOUTH AFRICA," ...HE SAID WITH A GRIN, 'I'VE GOT TO SEE SANTA-- NOW PLEASE LET ME IN !'"

"FATHER CHRISTMAS ," HE SAID. "IF I MAY BE SO BOLD-- THIS "SLEIGH-THING" IS TIRED... YOUR ACT'S GETTING OLD!"

"I'M A WRITER-PRODUCER, I'VE HAD MANY HITS. WHAT YOU NEED IS A **PLAY** WITH **GLAMOUR** AND **GLITZ**."

"WE'LL TOUR THE WHOLE WORLD ON HUGE FLATBED TRUCKS! WE'LL CHARGE MONEY FOR TICKETS! WE'LL BRING IN THE BUCKS!"

TICKETS

"WITH ELVES IN THE CHORUS AND REINDEER THAT DANCE! "SANTAFINA"--WE'LL CALL IT! IT'S YOUR BIG CHANCE!"

THIS SOUNDS MOST EXPENSIVE, HOW MUCH IS THE BILL?

WELL, NORMALLY LOTS! BUT FOR YOU-- 14 MILL!

THE ELVES SMILED AND GIGGLED. THE REINDEER MADE MERRY, AND THEN SANTA **LAUGHED** LIKE A BOWL FULL OF JELLY.

PAY 14 MILLION ?!...IS THAT WHAT IT'S WORTH ?! THERE'S NO ONE SO **STUPID** ON THE FACE OF THIS EARTH!

AND WITH THAT, OLD ST NICK GOT INTO HIS SLEIGH, AND DROPPED THE MAN OFF ON HIS WAY TO SA.

AND THEY HEARD HIM EXCLAIM AS HE DROVE OUT OF SIGHT--

"PEACE ON EARTH TO YOU ALL! MERRY CHRISTMAS, GOOD NIGHT!"

MADAM & EVE

BY S. FRANCIS, H. DUGMORE & RICO.

AHA! CAUGHT YOU!!

I'VE ALWAYS SUSPECTED THAT WHENEVER I LEAVE THE HOUSE YOU INVITE YOUR FRIENDS OVER AND HAVE A PARTY!!

WELL? WHAT HAVE YOU GOT TO SAY FOR YOURSELF?

SURPRISE!! HAPPY BIRTHDAY TO YOU! HAPPY BIRTHDAY TO YOU! HAPPY BIRTHDAY DEAR MADAM...

NICE TRY! BUT IT'S NOT MY BIRTHDAY.

WE WISH YOU A MERRY CHRISTMAS! WE WISH YOU A MERRY CHRISTMAS! WE WISH YOU...

...AND CHRISTMAS IS EIGHT MONTHS AWAY!!

ADMIT IT, EVE. I FINALLY CAUGHT YOU! IT TOOK ME A WHILE, BUT I FINALLY DID IT!! WHAT DO YOU SAY TO THAT?!

FOR SHE'S A JOLLY GOOD FELLOW! FOR SHE'S A JOLLY GOOD FEL-LOW!!

This wordless Christmas cartoon has become a classic — the expressions in the final panel capture South African reality, we think, with unusual poignancy.

LISTEN TO THIS, EVE ...

ACCORDING TO THE NEWSPAPER **THOUSANDS** OF PEOPLE ACTUALLY GET DEPRESSED OVER THE HOLIDAYS.

...INCREDIBLE, ISN'T IT?

Different generations often have problems communicating. This cartoon elicited a big response from many readers, including someone in England who e-mailed us to say it was her favourite cartoon of all time.

Continuing with the theme of embellishing CVs, inspired by the 'Makgoba Affair' at South Africa's largest university, we thought it would be funny to look at what it takes to be Father Christmas.

If anybody knows where you can actually get a figgy pudding in South Africa, please let us know before next Christmas ...

Unpack the silverware

What can we say? Sometimes a news story just begs to be turned into a Madam & Eve cartoon. For some strange reason, the new South African government, within days of being elected, decided to prove they were being 'transparent' by letting it be known that they had paid — wait for it — 2.4 million rands for new, imported silverware. Once again, these cartoons practically wrote themselves. In fact, we laid it on with a silver spoon.

Everyone always seems to feel sorry for squatters and homeless people — until the same people decide to move in across from you and create an 'informal settlement'. To illustrate our point, we created a homeless couple who move into Madam's back yard. They've been appearing regularly in Madam & Eve cartoons ever since.

MADAM & Eve

BY S.FRANCIS, H.DUGMORE & RICO

BEFORE I BEGIN THIS WEEK'S SERMON, I THINK IT'S TIME WE PASS AROUND THE *COLLECTION PLATE*.

AGAIN, REVEREND ALLAN?

OH, RIGHT. I FORGOT WE DID THAT ALREADY.

THE SOUTH AFRICAN CHURCH OF DANISH INVESTMENT

AND NOW, THOSE MEMBERS OF MY CONGREGATION WHO WISH TO BE *HEALED*, PLEASE COME FORTH.

WHAT IS YOUR PROBLEM, MY SON?

IT'S MY HUSBAND, REVEREND ALLAN. FOR THE PAST TWO YEARS HE'S BEEN UNABLE TO SPEAK.

NO PROBLEM! BY THE LAYING ON OF HANDS, I WILL CURE YOUR AFFLICTION!!

CLOSE YOUR EYES AND HAVE FAITH.

HEAL!!

HOW DO YOU FEEL, MY SON?

I...I...

HEY! MY WALLET'S GONE!!

IT'S A MIRACLE! HE CAN SPEAK!!

It's not a well-known fact, but the *Mail & Guardian*, wisely wishing to avoid lawsuits, regularly shows the Madam & Eve cartoon to their lawyers before they go to press. This one barely passed. We're not saying that 'Reverend Allan' in this cartoon is supposed to be Allan Boesak. (We're not denying it either.) Please don't sue us. Sue the *Mail & Guardian* — they're the ones who printed it first.

Hands up! How many of you bought the hardcover version of Nelson Mandela's *Long Walk To Freedom*? How many of you read it cover to cover? How many of you displayed it prominently in the lounge on your coffee table, even though you hadn't read it? What???? Liars, all of you!!!

...PLEASE? COME ON... JUST LET ME TRY **ONE** MORE TIME!

–SIGH.–

OKAY...NOW DON'T TELL ME! LET'S SEE... I GRAB YOUR HAND LIKE **THIS**...

...NOW HERE'S THE TRICKY PART. WAIT A MINUTE... HEY! I DID IT! **I DID IT!**

HILLARY! COME HERE! PRESIDENT MANDELA JUST TAUGHT ME THE AFRICAN HANDSHAKE.!!

AND, ACCORDING TO REPORTS, PRESIDENT MANDELA'S VISIT WITH U.S. PRESIDENT BILL CLINTON IS GOING EXTREMELY WELL.

SO TELL ME NELSON, WHY **EXACTLY** DO YOU NEED TO RAISE MONEY?

FOR RECONSTRUCTION AND DEVELOPMENT.

REALLY? MAYBE YOU SHOULD TALK TO MICHAEL JACKSON.

MICHAEL JACKSON?

YES, HE'S HAD **LOTS** OF RECONSTRUCTION AND DEVELOPMENT. ESPECIALLY ON HIS NOSE AND CHEEKBONES.

...COULD YOU SEE IF MY CHEQUE'S READY?

The historic meeting of two great world leaders. One plays the saxophone ... the other needs to raise money for his country. Sounded like a great idea for a cartoon to us.

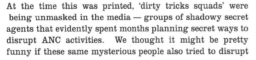

At the time this was printed, 'dirty tricks squads' were being unmasked in the media — groups of shadowy secret agents that evidently spent months planning secret ways to disrupt ANC activities. We thought it might be pretty funny if these same mysterious people also tried to disrupt the Madam & Eve cartoons with a campaign of cartoon dirty tricks. Anyway, we had a lot of fun doing these. This was also the only time Rico was allowed to spill ink on the cartoons on purpose. Boy, did he enjoy that!

We're including this cartoon because South African satirist Pieter-Dirk Uys told us it was one of his favourite cartoons and, this way, we get to casually drop his name in our book. We like it too.

Many Madam & Eve cartoons begin with the question 'What if?' We had read in the newspaper that in the spirit of reconciliation, Nelson Mandela was going to have tea with Mrs Betsy Verwoerd, octogenarian widow of Hendrik Verwoerd, the man considered to be the 'architect of apartheid'. So we began to think … What if she doesn't recognise him as the President? What if Nelson Mandela has so much fun, he begins visiting other conservative elderly white women for tea? What if he visits Mother Anderson? What if we just shut up and let you read the cartoons?

Actually, Nelson Mandela's shirts do match Stephen's curtains at home. Cartoonists don't make good interior designers.

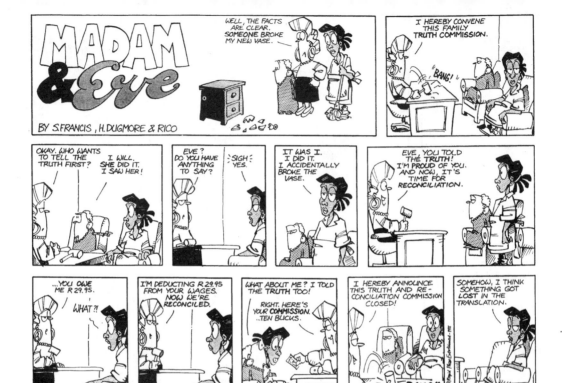

After it was announced that a Truth and Reconciliation Commission would be set up in South Africa, we thought it could be funny if Madam held her own 'truth and reconciliation commission' — but totally misunderstands the concept. This cartoon is famous — at least among us — for the incredible levitation trick Madam, Eve and Mother Anderson perform in the first panel. Rico denies it — but we say the way it was drawn, it looks like they're floating in the air. Maybe it's just an optical illusion.

Panel 1: THIS TRUTH COMMISSION DEMANDS THAT YOU GIVE US THE **TRUE FACTS** REGARDING YOUR DOMESTIC WORKER'S EMPLOYMENT!

Panel 2: ALRIGHT! ALRIGHT! I ADMIT IT! FOR YEARS AND YEARS I'VE PAID MY MAID ONLY 10 RAND A DAY!

Panel 3: I SEE...

Panel 4: IS SHE AVAILABLE TUESDAYS?

More cartoons on the truth commission — this time with Madam as the defendant and Eve as her lawyer. Luckily we did these cartoons weeks before the real Truth Commission began hearing evidence — otherwise they might not have seemed quite so funny. When it comes to humour, timing is everything. Also, notice how we re-used one of our first punch-lines, 'Is she available Tuesdays?' That's called a 'running gag' ... or laziness.

Panel 1: YOUR HONOUR... MAY I SUBMIT TO THE TRUTH COMMISSION EXHIBITS B, C AND D.

Panel 2: HAIR SAMPLES, CARPET SCRAPINGS AND ASSORTED FIBRES. / PROVING **WHAT**?

Panel 3: ..PROVING THAT I VACUUM ON A REGULAR BASIS.

Panel 4: **YOUR HONOUR!** I WISH TO **FIRE** MY LAWYER!! / NO WAY. WE **LIKE** HER.

15 It's so hard to tell a fairy tale in this country

Our main reason for creating Thandi, the baby sister of Eric's girlfriend Lizeka, was to set up a humorous contrast between the cynicism of Mother Anderson and the wide-eyed innocence of a really new South African. Somehow the chemistry between them just clicked ... and together they've become our favourite supporting players.

135

MADAM & Eve

BY S.FRANCIS, H.DUGMORE & RICO

YOU SURE *LOVE* THOSE GIN AND TONICS!

AND IN OTHER NEWS... FOLLOWING THE SILVER-WARE SCANDAL, THE DEBATE OVER THE GOVERNMENT *GRAVY TRAIN* CONTINUES...

WHAT'S A "GRAVY TRAIN"?

IT'S A BIG TRAIN THAT POLITICIANS LIKE TO GET ON.

ISN'T IT HARD TO RIDE A TRAIN FULL OF GRAVY?

YOU'D BE SURPRISED HOW *EASY* IT IS.

DO PRESIDENT MANDELA AND MISTER DE KLERK RIDE THE GRAVY TRAIN?

USUALLY.

DOES WINNIE MANDELA?

OH YES. I'D SAY SHE'S A REGULAR PASSENGER.

WHY DON'T THEY TAKE A *GRAVY BOAT* OR A *GRAVY AERO-PLANE*? IT WOULD GO A LOT FASTER.

GOOD IDEA.

I BET THE GRAVY'S GETTING REALLY *DEEP* NOW!

YOU COULD DEFINITELY SAY THAT.

DO THE POLITICIANS *KNOW* THEY'RE ALL FULL OF GRAVY?

YES, BUT THEY'RE IN DENIAL.

MOM! I'M LISTENING TO THIS!

This cartoon inspired the title of our fourth book, *Somewhere over the Rainbow Nation* (a reference to the song from *The Wizard of Oz*). We came up with the title of the book first, and then realised we had no cartoon to go with it. So we did this one. Usually it's the other way round.

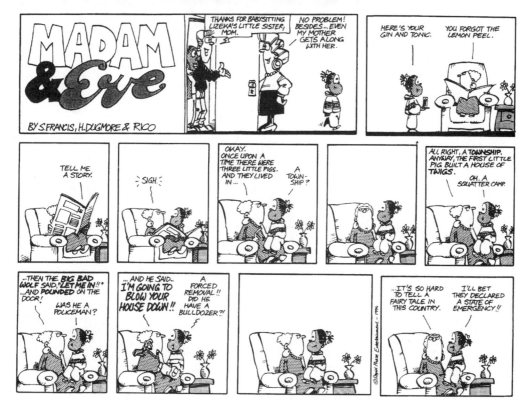

One of our top ten all-time favourite Madam & Eve cartoon strips.

16 Dali Tambo can paint?!

...AND IN OTHER NEWS, WINNIE MANDELA HAS BEGUN HER TENURE AS THE NEW DEPUTY MINISTER OF ARTS AND CULTURE.

ALTHOUGH MRS. MANDELA SAID SHE HAS A THOROUGH KNOWLEDGE OF ART AND ART HISTORY...

SHE *WILL*, HOWEVER, BE TAKING A SMALL REFRESHER COURSE...

AND *THIS* IS ONE OF DALI'S FAMOUS WORKS.

WAIT A MINUTE! DALI TAMBO CAN *PAINT*??!

AND THIS WEEK, NEW DEPUTY MINISTER WINNIE MANDELA CONTINUES HER REFRESHER COURSE IN ART, CULTURE AND SCIENCE...

OKAY, MRS. MANDELA. WE'VE COVERED "ART", LET'S SWITCH TO *SCIENCE*.

FINE WITH ME.

WE'LL BEGIN WITH PHYSICS. IF A BODY IS THROWN OFF A BUILDING, DOES THE VELOCITY INCREASE OR DECREASE?

DON'T LOOK AT ME! I WAS IN BRANDFORT.

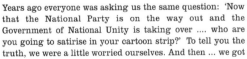

Years ago everyone was asking us the same question: 'Now that the National Party is on the way out and the Government of National Unity is taking over .... who are you going to satirise in your cartoon strip?' To tell you the truth, we were a little worried ourselves. And then ... we got a gift. A cartoonist's dream. Someone who was always in the news. Someone who was consistently controversial. Someone whose bodyguards even got into trouble. Winnie Mandela, we love you. And we thank you from the bottom of our inkwells. Keep up the good work.

"MY FIRST 100 DAYS AS PRESIDENT" ...BY NELSON MANDELA.

"MY FIRST 100 DAYS AS FIRST DEPUTY PRESIDENT" ...BY THABO MBEKI.

"MY FIRST 100 DAYS AS SECOND DEPUTY PRESIDENT" ...BY FW DE KLERK.

"MY FIRST 100 BODYGUARDS" ...BY WINNIE MANDELA.

GOOD NEWS, MISTER PRESIDENT. THE QUEEN WANTS TO **KNIGHT** YOU.

WHAT?!

BUT...IF SHE KNIGHTS **ME**, THAT WOULD MAKE WINNIE LADY MACBETH!

I MEAN, MANDELA. LADY **MANDELA**.

IT'S OKAY, SIR. FREUDIAN SLIP.

142

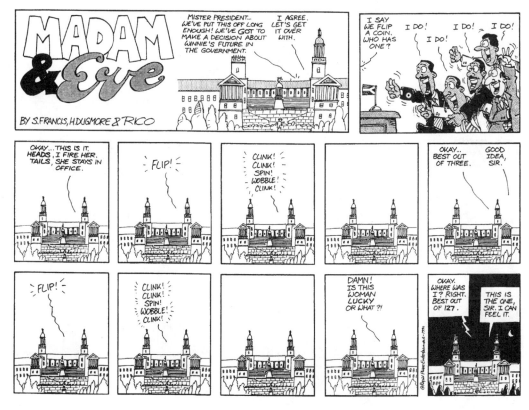

When Winnie was eventually removed from the Cabinet it was found that the government hadn't followed the correct procedures, and she had to be re-instated. And then, after that, she was fired all over again.

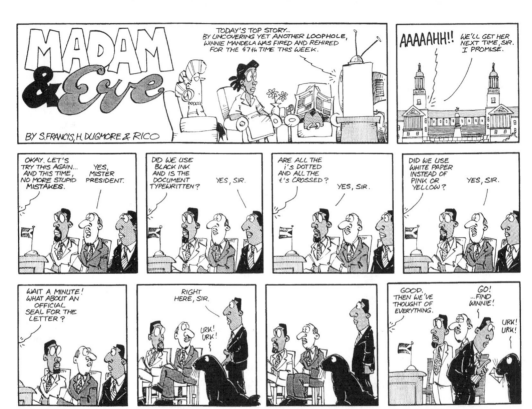

There was a time when it seemed that Winnie led a charmed life. Despite public promises that she would be fired from the Cabinet, for quite a while nothing happened, due largely to administrative bungling.

Based on the popular *Where's Wally* children's books, we decided to do a South African version entitled 'Where's Winnie?' Can you find her? Unfortunately, many readers couldn't — and some even complained to the newspaper. To locate Winnie, you have to know two things: one, she never travels without at least a half-dozen bodyguards; and two — whenever we drew her, she was always wearing the highly unusual green designer hat she wore at the Presidential inauguration.

17 **Bouncing off the walls**

You know that feeling when you get to work, and for some strange reason you're just not in the mood to work and you do everything possible to put off the work you have to do, and in fact you don't even want to talk to anyone because you feel like you're going crazy and your boss starts talking to you and you don't really hear what he or she is saying because you feel like ripping off all your clothes and dancing around the office naked? Don't you hate when that happens? Well, cartoonists have days like that too. That's when we decide to take a break from the serious issues of the day and just get ... wacky. Here's a selection of some of the wackiest Madam & Eve cartoons we've ever published. And yes, after we completed them, we ripped off all our clothes and danced around the office naked.

MADAM & Eve

BY S. FRANCIS, H. DUGMORE & RICO

HMMM... DUSTBINS FULL OF RUBBISH... FUZZBALLS ON THE RUG... DIRTY WINDOWS... THIS LOOKS LIKE A JOB FOR...

SUPERMAID!

USING HER POWERS OF **SUPER-SPEED**, SUPERMAID CLEANS THE LOUNGE IN MERE SECONDS!

AND YET, NO ONE WOULD SUSPECT THAT **SUPERMAID** IS ACTUALLY **EVE**... A MILD-MANNERED AND SEEMINGLY LAZY DOMESTIC MAINTENANCE ASSISTANT!

EVE! HAVE YOU DONE THE WASHING YET?!

UH-OH! THAT VOICE! IT CAN ONLY BE ONE PERSON... MY ARCH-NEMESIS... THE FIENDISH **DOCTOR MADAM**!

YOU CAN START WITH THE PILLOW-CASES. I LEFT THE **OMO** ON THE COUNTER.

A TRAP!!

GASP "**OMO-ITE**!" SUPERMAID'S ONE **WEAKNESS**! CHOKE FEEL WEAK... DIZZY...

... GOT TO REST... AND RECHARGE MY POWERS...

EVE! ARE YOU SLACKING OFF **AGAIN**?! HONESTLY... YOU'RE THE **LAZIEST** MAID I'VE EVER SEEN!!

LUCKILY, MY **SECRET IDENTITY** IS STILL SAFE.

Sometimes people ask us if we ever run out of ideas. The answer is 'Yes — every week.' But somehow we always manage to meet our deadlines. One time, though, we were stumped. No ideas came. Nothing. There's an old saying — 'Write what you know'. In this case, we decided to write what we didn't know and put Madam and Eve on an island in the ocean (an old cartoon cliché) until the 'writers' could come up with something funny. Believe it or not, we got several calls from readers who took us seriously — and wanted to know if our comedy well had really run dry. If so, they were willing to supply us with funny jokes — if the price was right. We politely declined. Luckily, our senses of humour returned by the next deadline.

A reader wrote in from Namibia and said the final panel of this cartoon was racist, as it used 'dumb Paddy' anti-Irish humour. Well, we got to say that not only do some of our best friends have best friends who are Irish, but we were amazed that the reader didn't have a problem with the derogatory ways we'd depicted all the other cultures. We've always prided ourselves on being equal opportunity offenders.

BY S. FRANCIS, H. DUGMORE & RICO.

EDITOR'S NOTE:

IN AN EFFORT TO EXPAND THEIR COMIC EMPIRE, THE AUTHORS ARE DEVELOPING SEVERAL NEW CARTOONS, UTILISING THE PROVEN MADAM & EVE FORMULA.

We debated whether we should include this in the book. Note the Christopher Reeve panel. Obviously, this was published a long time before his tragic accident.

As far as we can tell, the only good thing about traffic circles is that one of them inspired this cartoon.

MADAM & EVE BY S.FRANCIS, H.DUGMORE & RICO

MADAM! LOOK OUT!

CRASH! 24

IT'S ONE OF THOSE **EXTRA LARGE** MAIL & GUARDIAN PAGE NUMBERS.

THOSE THINGS ARE DEADLY IF THEY FALL OFF THE TOP OF THE PAGE.

LOOK MADAM! THE SHOCK-WAVES OPENED UP A HOLE IN THE SPACE-TIME CARTOON-STRIP CONTINULIM.

YOU MEAN...

YES! WE CAN LEAVE! WE'RE **FREE! FREE** FROM THE BOUNDARIES OF PEN & INK!

FREE TO EXPLORE **NEW** WORLDS...TO **BOLDLY GO** WHERE NO OTHER CARTOON CHARACTERS HAVE GONE BEFORE -- INTO THE REST OF THE NEWSPAPER.

EXCEPT FOR ONE PROBLEM.

THAT GRANDIOSE SPEECH YOU JUST MADE TOOK UP TWO PANELS... AND NOW THE HOLE IS WAY UP THERE.

THE LAWS OF CARTOON PHYSICS ARE TRULY AMAZING.

BUT HEY -- NO PROBLEM! ALL THE PANELS ARE WEAK...SEE?

COME. LET'S GO!

WAIT FOR ME!

MOM! WHAT ARE YOU DOING HERE?!

CIGARETTE BREAK. I'VE BEEN SNEAKING OUT FOR MONTHS.

The laws of cartoon physics are truly amazing. In fact, they're so complicated that Einstein didn't even come close to understanding them ... (We're of course talking about our neighbour, Bob Einstein, who lives down the block.) Anyway, we did this cartoon as our way to get back at the *Mail & Guardian*, who were once notorious for changing their newspaper format every month, especially the size of their page numbers.

18 Rolling the bones

OK, we admit it. As white guys, we love the legend of tokoloshes — weird little creatures that come to you in the middle of the night to carry you away. The only way to protect yourself is to put bricks under your bed, raising it off the floor. Luckily, we don't believe in stuff like this because all our astrological signs say we're not that gullible.

Sometimes we look back on our old cartoons and are amazed at how they almost predicted the future. In the early days of the strip, we wanted to create a new character, so we came up with the idea of a sangoma — but one who wears a three-piece suit, uses a cell phone and rolls the bones using a computer program. At the time, in 1992, it was unique. Now it's commonplace, or so we're told.

Not only is Elvis alive and well and living in South Africa — he even does his own shopping. Hey — he's got to buy his peanut butter and banana sandwiches somewhere! We got a call from the leading supermarket chain, Pick 'n Pay, asking to purchase the original cartoon artwork to hang in their CEO's office. Being nice guys (and incredibly stupid), we decided to donate it to the store and, as far as we know, these panels are framed and hanging in some Pick 'n Pay passage. If an executive from Pick 'n Pay is reading this, the least you could do is send us some boxes of free groceries.

We wanted to have some fun with Madam and her frequent visits to her shrink. Although we had already established in previous cartoon strips that Madam went to a white psychiatrist, we decided to change him slightly ... into a Rastafarian.

Dr Mabuza soon became a recurring character, giving psychiatric help to everyone, from Madam's mother to the entire Democratic Party.

The world is your mollusc

MRS ANDERSON...THIS IS VUSI. HE'LL BE WORKING ON YOUR TEETH TODAY.

MMPH?!

WE'VE JUST HIRED VUSI AS PART OF OUR NEW **AFFIRMATIVE ACTION** DENTAL TRAINING PROGRAM.

YES! I'M VERY EXCITED! YOU'RE MY FIRST... MY FIRST...

"PATIENT", VUSI. WE CALL THEM... "PATIENTS".

EVE!!

I'M SORRY, DOCTOR! I REFUSE TO LET SOME INEXPERIENCED INTERN PRACTICE ON **MY TEETH.**

DON'T YOU SUPPORT **AFFIRMATIVE ACTION**, MRS ANDERSON?

YES, OF COURSE. BUT--

OKAY, VUSI. LET'S BEGIN.

GOOD. I'LL GET THE PLIER THING.

"PLIER THING!?"

HE MEANS FORCEPS. IT'S A COMMON MISTAKE.

Some of the most widely quoted Madam & Eve cartoons of all time are those we have done on affirmative action. Like elsewhere in the world, this is a real hot button in the New South Africa — and we like pushing people's buttons.

OKAY ERIC! SMILE!

SMILE?! HOW CAN I SMILE?! I HAVE NO FUTURE! NONE!

THERE'S NO JOBS OUT THERE! DO YOU HEAR ME?! IT'S HOPELESS!!

SOB WHY DID I HAVE TO BE BORN WHITE?!

...GRADUATION JITTERS.

AS THIS YEAR'S FIRST GRADUATING CLASS IN THE NEW SOUTH AFRICA, I CONGRATULATE YOU.

FOR YOU, THIS IS A MOMENTOUS OCCASION. A TIME FOR NEW OPPORTUNITIES, PROSPERITY AND OPTIMISM AS YOU SEEK OUT CHALLENGING CAREERS.

THE FUTURE IS YOURS! EMBRACE IT WITH OPEN ARMS AS YOU FULFIL EACH AND EVERY ONE OF YOUR DREAMS! ...THANK YOU.

RIGHT. THAT COVERS THE BLACK GRADUATES. AND NOW, A BRIEF MESSAGE FOR ALL THE WHITE GRADUATES...

UH-OH. OOOO.

169

AND I SAY TO OUR WHITE GRADUATES-- STOP BEING SO NEGATIVE AND PESSIMISTIC!

I'M SURE THERE'S **SOMETHING** IN YOUR FUTURE YOU CAN LOOK FORWARD TO! THINK ABOUT IT!

...YES? THE WHITE GRADUATE IN THE FOURTH ROW.

WELL, THE ROLLING STONES ARE COMING IN FEBRUARY.

SEE?! THERE YOU GO!

AND IN CONCLUSION, GRADUATES... GO OUT THERE AND MAKE YOUR CONTRIBUTION TO THE NEW SOUTH AFRICA. THE WORLD IS YOUR OYSTER.

WHAT ABOUT THE WHITE STUDENTS, SIR?

GOOD POINT.

AND, FOR THE WHITE GRADUATES, EVEN THOUGH THE WORLD MIGHT **NOT** BE YOUR **OYSTER**, IT CAN STILL BE YOUR-- YOUR...

TOUGH METAPHOR. WHAT'S A LESSER SHELLFISH?

MOLLUSK?

White graduates were complaining that they no longer automatically get jobs, like in the 'good old days'. That might be true in some cases, but recent figures show that even though many companies have affirmative action programmes, white graduates are still getting most of the top jobs.

The affirmative action hostage drama cartoons, starring university buddies Sipho and Eric, caused quite a stir and were reprinted by newspapers all over the world, including *The Wall Street Journal* and *The Economist*.

We're 'big' in Denmark!

Who knew? When we first began Madam & Eve we considered ourselves lucky that a single newspaper would publish our cartoons, let alone pay us. Amazingly, our cartoon strips now reach almost five million South Africans in eight daily newspapers, four weekly newspapers, and three national magazines. We've also produced four best-selling Madam & Eve book collections. And Madam & Eve cartoons appear in magazines and books in Danish, Swedish and Norwegian, with, if we're lucky, other countries coming on board soon.

Madam & Eve cartoons have also appeared — with accompanying articles — in international publications from the *New York Times* to *Newsweek*. As the strip's creators, we've been interviewed by major television stations from around the world, including some where we couldn't understand the questions (which we hope was because they spoke in a foreign language).

So. Why has a cartoon about a South African suburban madam and her wisecracking domestic worker become so popular?

THE NEW YORK TIMES **INTERNATIONAL** *MONDAY, APRIL 5, 1993*

Johannesburg Journal

Time to Laugh? The Beloved Country Thinks So

Getting Madam & Eve into the *New York Times* was a big thrill, particularly for Stephen, whose New Jersey-based parents have read the NYT every morning for fifty years. Someone in the Disney organisation saw the article, and we were asked to donate the original artwork of the cartoon 'Is she available Tuesdays' to the Disney cartoon museum. We were glad to do so — and delighted to receive a hand-painted Mickey Mouse animation cell in return. The power of the press!

Partly, we think, because it's topical. And partly because it uses satire to subvert and challenge racial and ethnic stereotypes. And also because South Africans are learning to laugh at themselves.

These are some of the reasons we've heard — and some of them we've even offered ourselves during interviews. But the truth is, we don't really know. We like to think, in our less modest moments, that it may be because the cartoons are funny.

Trouble with the servants

OF ALL the insecurities of post-apartheid South Africa, none is quite so perplexing as the question of how to treat the servants. The third world over, maids, cooks, nannies and gardeners are common conveniences for the rich, and even the not so rich, because they are cheap and affordable. Nowhere does the relationship between a wh... decide to keep her. Once you have employed a maid, you belong to the informal African job network; she may well appeal to you for help in finding a nice white madam for her daughter or her niece. It is not unknown for the daughter of a white madam...

... ironies," says Harry Dugmore, one of the three creators of Madam & Eve, the country's best-known cartoon strip, which plays on the absurdities of this microcosm of South African race relations, "but in social terms they are bitter realities, because the intimacy is completely false." Madam & Eve began life in 1992, two years after Nelson Mandela was released from jail and when South Africans were just beginning to laugh at themselves. It aims to subvert, not uphold, the stereotype. Madam says things that whites no longer dare: "Why all a black...

THE WASHINGTON POST
WORLD NEWS

Finding S. Africa's Funny Bone
Comic Strip Targets Issues That Once Were No Laughing Matter

By Paul Taylor
Washington Post Foreign Service

JOHANNESBURG

The first thing Stephen Francis noticed when he moved to South Africa was that a lot of people called his wife "madam."

"Strange," he remembers thinking. "Where I come from, 'madam' means something very different." Francis comes from New York.

Here, it means that a black person of a certain station—a maid, gardener, gas station attendant, grocery store checker, tea maker, hawker, whatever—is speaking to a white woman. If it's a white man, the equivalent salutation is "boss."

The apartheid system of racial separation may be dead in South Africa, but vestiges of a centuries-old racial caste system linger. Francis is a comedy writer, and he figured he could do a brisk business in the chasm between South Africa's social and political realities.

With two collaborators, he created "Madam and Eve," a comic strip that satirizes the new South Africa through the old-fashioned relationship of a white employer and her live-in black maid. It has become popular, and seems to have located a common national funny bone in a society that never realized it had one.

Eve is lup, assertive and modern. Madam is pennypinching and dense and troubled by nightmares of the huge mounds of coffee and sugar she imagines Eve has been stealing in spoonfuls for the last 20 years and squirreling away in her servant's quarters.

The supporting cast includes Madam's mother from England, who engages Eve in conversation with openers on the order of: "I know a black boy in London. His name is Leroy. Do you know him?"

In the grand tradition of underdog humor, Madam gets her comeuppance more often than Eve. But the strip pokes fun across lines of color and caste. Its theme is to explore the ways people can stare an intimate space and yet remain strangers.

There are roughly 1 million black maids in South Africa, most of whom live with their white employers and sometimes raise their own families there. They bring up the children, prepare the meals and wash the clothes of the nation's 5 million whites.

Francis, 38, met his South African wife while she was working for her country's consulate in New York. When they moved here five years ago, he had no idea what to expect. "From what I'd seen on television, I figured I'd spend a lot of time driving through burning townships, and have to stop for the occasional lion crossing."

Instead, he found suburbs that looked a lot like the United States. But he ran into oddities as well—none more alien to his egalitarian sensibility than black-white relationships that seemed frozen in colonial-era rigidities of manners, customs and mores.

"The first place I worked, a black tea lady came into the office every morning at 11 to serve the staff," he recalled. "I was so uncomfortable, I didn't know what to do with myself. On the second day, I said to her, 'Why don't I make something for you?' She looked at me like I was crazy, but I made her coffee. Then I found it was awkward to stop doing it, so I made her coffee every day."

Francis's collaborators, Harry Dugmore, 32, and Rico Schacherl, 27, say you don't need to be a foreigner to share Francis's discomfort. "Whites of our generation cringe at certain social situations you still

See JOKES, A36, Col. 1

Stephen Francis's comic strip satirizes the relationship between a black maid and her white employer.

This article focused strongly on Stephen, an American doing something 'unusual' in South Africa. We were excited to be in *The Washington Post*, the paper that all US presidents read. We wondered if Bill read this article. We hoped that he had, but he didn't call to chat, which was a little disappointing.

Early in 1997 *The Economist* ran a thoughtful piece on the changing position of domestic workers in South Africa. They also ran our well-known 'Free at Last' cartoon.

La nouvelle société sud-africaine au crible de la BD

La bande dessinée «Madame et Eve», qui met en scène une patronne blanche et sa femme de ménage noire, est devenue en treize mois un succès commercial... qui tente la télévision.

Johannesburg, de notre correspondante

Sur un mur de l'austère quartier des affaires de Johannesburg, un graffiti déstabilise «Madame et Eve, Président!» Une perspective malheureusement tout aussi improbable que le mariage dont l'autre couple historique du moment—Nelson Mandela & Frederik De Klerk—ignore si Madame et Eve les a largement supplantés au barmètre de popularité. Car, Gwen Anderson, la patronne blanche, et Eve Sisulu, sa «coordinatrice» selon de maladroisante domestique» selon le langage (presque) politiquement correct en Afrique du Sud, n'existent que sur le papier. Celui de trois journaux, quotidiens et hebdomadaires, et maintenant un livre, qu'elles égayent de la plus décapante bande dessinée sud-africaine.

Il n'y a guère qu'un pays au monde... C'est encore au même «point» que se focalisent les préjugés, les suspicions et les peurs entre les deux communautés. Ref, grâce au regard incisif d'un Américain en villégiature, Madame et Eve est instantanément devenu l'emblème de la psyché sud-africaine.

«Au départ, je ne comprenais pas pourquoi, malgré ses injonctions, la domestique appelait toujours femme "Madame" et mon "Baas" (patron en afrikaans). Puis, j'ai découvert ce formidable univers des "Madames" qui partagent avec leurs domestiques leurs plus intimes secrets mais ne connaissent pas leurs noms de familles», explique Stephen Francis. Marié à une Sud-Africaine, le Californien vécut, il y a quelques années, après sa rencontre avec l'auteur burzolatie, Harry Dugmore, et le dessinateur Rico... tranchées, «Madame» à la coiffure en suspension et les escarpins renforcés des meilleures caricatures de Margaret Thatcher. Elle, à aussi son pragmatisme économique dans ce cas, retranché à souffrir d'une sondaine aubade à chaque évocation par Eve d'une augmentation de salaire. Pourtant Gwen Anderson, avec son statut de divorcée et ses boucles d'oreilles «olé-olé», des prétentions de libérale des banlieues nord de Johannesburg. En réalité, comme la plupart de ses compatriotes, «Madame tente de s'accrocher à la nouvelle Afrique du Sud. C'est dur, elle lutte, se débat», précise Stephen Francis.

Eve est son guide, commentant par le biais de la idée ce nouvel univers environnant la cellule indissociable et retranchée; la maison de Madame. Lorsqu'elle n'a pas décidé de jouer... tion de se rendre «au petit coin». Madame lui précise le chemin suivant le salon avec sa télé et la vidéo «usuelles», pois tournant devant sa chambre «où dort un vieux rottweiler» qui garde des «bijoux, imitations sans valeur». Pois, par acquis de conscience, elle demande à Eve de ne s'arrêter à aucun des «sièges de WC», dit Eve à Madame couvrit déjà à la poussette de son précieux bien. Pourtant Eve et son panoplie, exempte de défauts. Si Madame de faire remarquer à son employée qui réclame un «congé d'urgence» pour enterrer son oncle qu'il est déjà mort, trois fois.

Avec Madame et Eve, ce sont tous les syndromes d'une société schizophrène et fortement paranoïaque qui ressortent: voitures de luxe et glaciaos, systèmes d'alarme et sorcières, C'est...

We've also been fortunate in our press coverage in Europe. This article appeared in *Liberation* in France in 1994. We think the headline says something like 'the new South African society learns to laugh'.

In 1996, our second Danish book appeared, entitled *Personally, I blame Mandela for this.* The book got a huge review in a major Danish newspaper which helped to boost sales.

We would never have predicted that Denmark would be the first country to translate Madam & Eve. Our first Danish book appeared in 1995, with the title, roughly translated, *I'm sorry Madam, but Black Coffee is now in Fashion.* Gyldendal, our Danish publisher, is one of the oldest publishing houses in Europe, and has a fine tradition of bringing foreign works to Danish readers.

We have no way of checking on the accuracy of foreign language translations; we just hope that all the nuance, such as it is, is kept in.

Madam & Eve appears in the comic magazines LARSON! and ERNIE in Sweden and Norway. Both magazines ran the strips as an experiment, but they proved popular and Madam & Eve now appears regularly in both.

LOOK EVE. A LETTER FOR ME MAILED ONLY THREE DAYS AGO.

THE POSTAL SERVICE IS IMPROVING!

181

MADAM & Eve

BY S.FRANCIS, H.DUGMORE & RICO

IT WAS A HOT, DRY DAY WHEN THE STRANGER CAME TO TOWN...

WHO SHE WAS OR WHERE SHE CAME FROM, NOBODY KNOWS.

SENSING TROUBLE, THE PIANO PLAYER STOPPED WHEN SHE WALKED THROUGH THE DOORS OF THE DOUBLE-R-SALOON.

THE GAMBLERS DROPPED THEIR CARDS...

... AND THE BARTENDER KEPT HIS HANDS IN PLAIN SIGHT.

EVEN THE SALOON GIRLS KEPT THEIR DISTANCE...

FINALLY, A YOUNG COWBOY AT THE BAR HAD THE COURAGE TO ASK HER NAME.

MY NAME IS EVE.

...SHE SAID.

...AND I'M GOING TO CLEAN UP THIS TOWN!

POP!!

HUH?

EVE! WAKE UP! GET BACK TO WORK!!

BUT... I HAVEN'T CLEANED UP THE TOWN YET.

FORGET THE TOWN. JUST CLEAN UP THE KITCHEN.

Our first four Madam & Eve book covers. Creating a cover that 'jumps out' at consumers and screams 'buy me!' is not easy. We spend weeks experimenting with each cover design until we think we're happy. Then we usually change our minds and start again. Bringing out an annual Madam & Eve compilation has now become a tradition ...

22 Go publish yourself!

The book you're now holding is our fifth Madam & Eve book. It's published by Penguin Books ... and they asked us to mention that if you're still standing in the book store reading this, go pay for it already! In fact, just about all our cartoon collections are published by Penguin Books. All, that is, except for our very first book. And that was an entirely different story.

In 1993, after working on Madam & Eve for twelve months, it suddenly hit us. We had accumulated enough cartoons for ... *a book!* We were elated. Elated and excited. And, since more and more newspapers seemed to be interested in publishing our cartoon, our book *had* to be a best-seller! We were going to be rich beyond our wildest dreams!

And then we did a little research.

We found out, for example, that whatever your book sells for, a big portion of that price goes to the book store. Then the publisher takes a percentage to cover their overhead, printing bills, distribution costs etc. After everything is deducted, this generally leaves the author with a royalty in the neighbourhood of ... well, let's just say it's a very small neighbourhood. And, since there were three of us, it meant splitting the proceeds three ways.

Maybe we weren't going to be as rich as we thought.

But hey — we're creative guys. So we came up with a great idea: *Why not publish the book ourselves?!*

It was a stroke of genius. Sure, we'd still have to give a big portion of the selling price to the book store, but the rest was all ours! Well, sort of.

We needed a partner. Some sucker who would not only front us the R150 000 for the printing bill, but would also help sell the book to book stores and, most importantly, collect the money. That sucker was the *Weekly Mail*, the first newspaper to publish Madam & Eve. And so we formed a partnership. They put up the money. We put up the cartoons.

In the end, our first book, *The Madam & Eve Collection*, did very well, selling out its initial printrun, and a reprint. In total, 23 000 copies were sold in a country where selling 5 000 copies makes a book a best-seller.

Oddly enough, that first book is considered a collector's item today, with books in mint condition fetching over R200 at specialist book shops. The *Weekly Mail* and ourselves did very well indeed. So, you're probably wondering why, if publishing our own books was so profitable, how come we never did it again?

Simple. It was hard work. Together with some staff from the *Weekly Mail*, we had to arrange *everything ourselves*. The marketing. The promotion.

The publicity. The advertising and selling. The distribution. We even stayed up nights, cutting out and pasting together hundreds of promotional book displays out of painted cardboard.

That's why, when it came time for the next book, we decieded to go with a real publisher, Penguin Books. They put up the money, do all of the logistics, and make sure the books gets into the book stores. So far, each Madam & Eve book published by Penguin has reached the number one position and stayed on the best-seller list for three to four months.

In fact, when our third cartoon collection, *All Aboard For the Gravy Train*, hit number one, it knocked a book by a first-time author, *Long Walk To Freedom*, to the number two position.

So naturally, since *Madam & Eve's Greatest Hits* is a special collection — commemorating five years of publication — we're hoping that this collection is just as successful as the others. So if you're *still* standing in the book shop reading this book standing up, will you please *get in the queue and pay for it already??* We need the royalty. And remember, when it comes time to split the proceeds, there are three of us. And to those of you who have already bought this book, or have received it as a gift, our warmest gratitude.

For our 1996 book, we were stumped for a title. Somehow the words 'Rambo Nation' popped into our heads. 1996 was a tough year for South Africa. The Rand dived to a record low, and crime sky-rocketed to a record high. And we came up with this cover in that light. On reflection, however, we thought it was too cynical and considered an alternative title: *Somewhere over the Rainbow Nation*. This, we thought, had a much better ring to it, and it eventually became the title of our fourth book. The original almost-a-cover still makes us laugh though, and we've kept it as a reminder of what might have been.

In 1995 we brought out the first Madam & Eve *One Day at a Time* desk calendar. The only problem was that the calendars got into the shops two days before Christmas because of production glitches. So they didn't sell particularly well. In 1996 we got the desk calendars out to bookshops much earlier, and sales were brisk. In retail, as in comedy, timing is everything.

23 This dummy's worth nine hundred bucks!

Quick — what's the fastest growing industry in South Africa today? The correct answer is 'security companies'. (If you said burglary, car hijacking or bank robbery, you're also right.) The simple truth is ... crime touches everyone in this country, whatever your race, whatever your background. Luckily, however, for cartoonists, crime — and the seemingly total inability of governments to control it — can be a great subject to satirise. The bad news is that many of these cartoons were written five years ago — and they're more relevant than ever.

MADAM & Eve

BY S. FRANCIS, H. DUGMORE & RICO

STICK 'EM UP.

MADAM!! IT'S FOR YOU!

HI, JOHN JACKSON... "FIRST STRIKE SECURITY." SORRY IF I SCARED YOU, BUT I HAD TO DEMONSTRATE HOW PITIFULLY VULNERABLE YOU ARE WITHOUT A GOOD SECURITY SYSTEM.

I SEE YOUR MAID WANTS TO KILL ME RIGHT NOW. IT'S A COMMON REACTION. HERE... HAVE A BROCHURE.

YOU'VE HEARD OF "ARMED RESPONSE," RIGHT? WELL, WE OFFER A DELUXE VERSION...

"ARMED NUCLEAR RESPONSE!"

...ARMED NUCLEAR RESPONSE?

YES. SOMEONE TRIPS THE SILENT ALARM AND WE NUKE YOUR HOUSE FROM AN AERIAL ATTACK. WIPES OUT ALL CRIMINALS AT GROUND ZERO.

NUKE MY HOUSE?

HEY... WE'RE VERY ACCURATE.

SLAM!

WUP! WUP! WUP! WUP!

SALES LEADER TO CHOPPER ONE. CANCEL THE FREE DEMONSTRATION.

When we saw in news reports that over 6 800 prisoners had escaped from police custody in one year, we couldn't resist. Now if we could just get all of them to buy a copy of this book ...

190

Don't laugh. When we wrote this cartoon, all three of us were burgled within a three-week period. And for once, we're not joking.

We're not sure, but we think South Africans perfected the 'go-slow' type of protest, where the employees don't actually boycott their jobs ... they just perform their duties very ... well, slowly. And yes, even the police go on go-slows. We just wish sometimes they'd try protesting with a 'go-fast'.

One of our silliest cartoons and also one of our favourites.
Probably because everyone who reads it can relate to it.
We don't know about you, but hardly a weekend goes by
without this happening to us. After a while, you just learn
to ignore it.

To celebrate South Africa's hosting of, and eventual triumph in the Rugby World Cup, Madam & Eve went where no cartoons have gone before: into the heart of rugby football. These signals are based on real rugby referee signals. Study them and memorise them. There's a quiz at the end of the book.

WHAT A DAY FOR SPORT AND POLITICS! THE ANC AND THE IFP HAVE DECIDED TO RESOLVE THEIR DIFFERENCES WITH A GAME OF RUGBY!

AND HERE COMES THE ANC TEAM LED BY CAPTAIN MANDELA!

AND HERE COMES THE IFP TEAM LED BY CAPTAIN BUTHELEZI!

WAIT A MINUTE! THERE'S SOME COMMOTION ON THE FIELD! THE IFP ARE **MOVING** THE GOALPOSTS!

THE ANC-IFP **RUGBY** GAME IS ABOUT TO BEGIN! TEAM CAPTAINS MANDELA AND BUTHELEZI ARE IN THE CENTRE OF THE FIELD FOR THE COIN TOSS...

AND ALLAN BOESAK HAS JUST FLIPPED THE COIN!

THAT'S STRANGE. THE COIN SEEMS TO HAVE GONE MISSING.

When South Africa won the Rugby World Cup everyone celebrated, including Mother Anderson. We presented this cartoon personally to Francois Pienaar as a gift, shortly after the World Cup triumph. It could be hanging right now in his bar. Or in his room. Or in his basement.

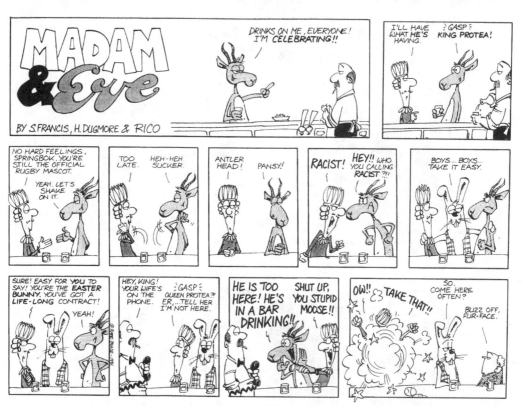

After the World Cup, there was this huge debate: should South Africa replace the Springbok as a symbol of rugby with the King Protea — a flower??! We thought it might be interesting if the two of them met in a bar. And it gave Rico the opportunity to draw cartoon animals, which we all love because he makes them so damn funny.

25 Get that koeksister out of your pocket

EVE... I'M GAINING **WEIGHT!** FROM NOW ON, YOUR NEW JOB IS TO **STOP** ME FROM OVER-EATING! DO WHAT-EVER IT TAKES! I'M COUNTING ON YOU!

..KIND OF LIKE... "THE **DIET POLICE!**"

EXACTLY!

"DIET POLICE" — I LOVE IT! UNLIMITED AUTHORITY! SEARCHES AND SEIZURES! UNLAWFUL WARRANTS! HARSH FINES! BREAKING INTO THE WRONG HOUSE!

...GIVE SOMEONE A LITTLE **POWER** AND IT GOES STRAIGHT TO THEIR **HEAD.**

...OF COURSE, I'LL HAVE TO HAVE A UNIFORM...

FREEZE! DIET POLICE!

CLICK!

RAISE YOUR ARMS SLOWLY AND STEP AWAY FROM THAT FRIED CHICKEN!!

I MUST'VE BEEN CRAZY TO AGREE TO THIS.

Although Madam & Eve is generally considered to be a topical, issue-driven cartoon strip, sometimes our most popular cartoons turn out to be situations based on every-day domestic relationships — and not newspaper head-lines. Here are some of our favourite domestic cartoon strips.

Our famous Parktown prawn strip. We all agreed that these goofy insects could become regular characters in the strip. For some reason, they never appeared again. Go figure.

Harry's personal number one favourite Madam & Eve four-panel cartoon.

We don't know about you, but living in South Africa, when we hear the word 'highway', we think of 'hijacking', 'under construction' and 'potholes'. So when we heard 'Information highway', we got the idea for this cartoon.

MADAM & EVE

BY S. FRANCIS, H. DUGMORE & RICO

...AND THAT'S WHAT **ANNOYS** MY MADAM THE MOST.

OKAY, WHO'S NEXT?

ME, ME!

MY TURN!

HERE'S A GOOD ONE. I ALWAYS WAIT UNTIL MY MADAM GETS **REALLY** COMFORTABLE, SITTING IN THE LOUNGE--

...AND THEN I START TO VACUUM!

HEE HEE! ME TOO!

HAHAHA! I DO THAT ALSO!

TRY THIS... "ACCIDENTALLY" LEAVE A TUBE OF NAPPY RASH CREAM BY THEIR TOOTH-BRUSH...

YOU MEAN...

NEVER FAILS! THEY BRUSH THEIR TEETH WITH IT!

HAHAHAHA!

WHAT ABOUT PUTTING TOO MUCH STARCH IN THEIR UNDER-WEAR!!

YES! YES! OR RUN-NING A HOT TAP WHEN THEY TAKE A SHOWER?!

HA HA HEE HEE

HA HEE HEE

HA HA! HEE HEE HA!

HAHAHA! HEE HEE HAHA

≥SIGH≤   ≥SIGH≤   ≥SIGH.≤

EVE! CAN'T YOU DO A WASH PROPERLY?! I CAN'T FIND ANY OF MY LEFT SOCKS!!

BWA-HAHA! HA HA HA! HA! HA HA HA!

HEE-HEE! GOOD ONE! HEE-HEE! HA HA!

HAHAHA! I'VE GOT TO TRY THAT ONE! HEE HEE HEE!

© Rapid/Rico Entertainment 1998

Cellular madness — South Africa now has the second biggest cellular network in the world. With Telkom's levels of service, it's no wonder.

EVE'S THE ONLY PERSON I KNOW WHO CAN FALL *ASLEEP* ON AN IRONING BOARD.

AND BEST YET, IT'S STILL WARM.

THIS IS RIDICULOUS.

EVE!! DON'T YOU EVER GET *TIRED* OF *SLEEPING ON THE IRONING BOARD?!!*

Somehow, we came up with the idea of Eve taking naps on her ironing board. Where did we get such a crazy notion? Could it have had anything to do with Snoopy of the Peanuts strip taking naps on the roof of his dog house? Nah. Not us. Besides, we'd never admit it, anyway.

212

Remember when one rand bought you two U.S. dollars?
Remember when one rand was printed on paper!?

These cartoons are based on a supposedly true story. Suddenly our phone began ringing off the hook. Family and friends were calling, telling us to quickly turn on the radio. It seemed there was a discussion about madams and maids going on. One of the callers told a story about how he had hidden a video camera in his cupboard when things began disappearing from his house — and caught his maid red-handed. Sort of ... 'Smile, you're on candid camera — you're fired.' Although it sounded a little fishy, we thought it would make a great cartoon strip.

Climb every mountain

South Africa's first large-scale expedition to conquer Everest was beset with problems from the very beginning. The selection process for women climbers was dubious at best, and once the crew got to Everest, half the team resigned. From then, things just went from bad to worse, and one of the sponsors, *The Sunday Times*, cancelled the rest of their sponsorship after their reporters were allegedly abused by the expedition leader. We tried to find a little humour among the tragedy.

Madam and Eve, however, had a far less traumatic time climbing up Everest.

25 There's no business like show business

After Nelson Mandela's book came out, Hollywood producers were clamouring for the rights. The following conversation actually took place. Honest!

A QUIET RURAL VILLAGE, SOUTH OF THE LIMPOPO.

SUDDENLY, THE SILENCE IS BROKEN... BY TWO DOZEN SPEEDING LIMOUSINES...

WHAT IS IT, MOMMY?! IS MADIBA COMING?!

NO... IT'S SARAFINA II!!

LOOK MOMMY! ...HELICOPTERS!

OKAY, EVERYONE. THIS IS THE PLACE. LAND THE HELICOPTERS AND PARK THE AIR CONDITIONED BUSES!

HEY, KID. WE'RE THE SARAFINA II TOURING COMPANY. WHERE'S YOUR THEATRE?

THEATRE? THIS IS A SMALL VILLAGE. WE DON'T HAVE A THEATRE.

NO PROBLEM, KID. WE'LL BUILD ONE.

HEY! SOMEBODY GET ME THE CHEQUEBOOK!!

WE FORGOT TO BRING IT, SIR. CAN WE USE PETTY CASH?

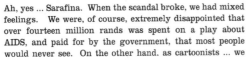

Ah, yes ... Sarafina. When the scandal broke, we had mixed feelings. We were, of course, extremely disappointed that over fourteen million rands was spent on a play about AIDS, and paid for by the government, that most people would never see. On the other hand, as cartoonists ... we were overjoyed. Thank you, Minister of Health, Dr Zuma. Even if we had made this stuff up, no one would believe us. It was the new South African government's first real scandal — and we were right there with our pens and ink. Hey — there's no business like show business.

MADAM&Eve

presents:

UPCOMING
14 MILLION RAND
MUSICALS

...WITH AN EDUCATIONAL MESSAGE.

BY S.FRANCIS, H.DUGMORE & RICO

PARAFFINA

INSTRUCTS THE SAFE USE OF PARAFFIN AND FIRE PREVENTION.

SAHARAFINA

TEACHES ABOUT THE HAZARDS OF GETTING LOST IN THE DESERT.

LAVAFINA

WARNS OF THE DANGERS OF LIVING TOO CLOSE TO AN ACTIVE VOLCANO.

HIJACKAFINA

IMPARTS SAFETY TIPS FOR MOTORISTS IN EXPENSIVE CARS.

SARAFINA-II-FINA

TEACHES POLITICIANS THE WISDOM OF SPENDING 14 MILLION ON AN EDUCATIONAL MUSICAL.

STEP ONE: WE ARGUE ABOUT THE SUBJECT OF THE CARTOON.

RAPID PHASE

WHAT'S SO FUNNY ABOUT THAT?!

WE ALREADY DID THAT!

ARE YOU CRAZY?!

STEP TWO: WE FINALLY PIN DOWN THE SUBJECT AS THE DEADLINE APPROACHES.

ARE YOU CRAZY?!

RAPID PHASE

WE DID THAT ALREADY!

THAT'S FUNNY???

IF WE CAN'T COME WITH A GOOD IDEA **OURSELVES**, THEN WE USUALLY GO TO AN IDEA STORE.

CAN I HELP YOU?

YES. WE NEED A FUNNY IDEA FOR A CARTOON... **QUICKLY!**

IDEA STORE

TODAY'S SPECIALS:

PEOPLE OFTEN ASK US "WHERE DO WE GET OUR IDEAS?" THIS IS WHERE WE GET A LOT OF THEM. UNFORTUNATELY, GOOD IDEAS DON'T COME CHEAP.

GOT ONE RIGHT HERE. IT WAS ALMOST USED BY GARY LARSON OF THE "FAR SIDE". BUT FOR YOU-- HALF PRICE.

WE'LL TAKE IT!

STEP THREE: WE LOCK STEPHEN AWAY IN HIS OFFICE UNTIL...

Okay, Eve. I read the New Labour Relations Act. I'm ready to Negotiate.

Negotiate!!

There's Nothing to Negotiate. It's all there in Black + White!

Let me rephrase that.

... HE'S WRITTEN A "ROUGH VERSION" OF THE CARTOON WHICH INCLUDES THE BASIC DIALOG.

THIS CAN GET EITHER ONE OF TWO REACTIONS...

GOOD REACTION

HAHAHAHAHA!!

BAD REACTION

THAT'S FUNNY???

WE ALREADY DID THAT.

STEP FIVE: WE GIVE THE "ROUGH" TO RICO, WHO WILL BEGIN TO "PENCIL" THE STRIP USING...

A PENCIL.

THE "PENCIL VERSION" CAN GIVE A GOOD IDEA OF WHAT THE FINISHED CARTOON WILL LOOK LIKE.

HMMM...

HMMM...

LET ME REPHRASE THAT.

THIS IS ALSO A GOOD TIME TO DISCUSS CHANGES IN THE DIALOG OR THE DRAWINGS.

THAT'S FUNNY?!

ARE YOU CRAZY?!

DIDN'T WE DO THAT ALREADY?!

STEP SIX: WHEN EVERYONE AGREES, THE PENCIL VERSION IS NOW "INKED" USING...

INK.

PEOPLE ALSO OFTEN ASK US **HOW** WE MANAGE TO MEET OUR DEADLINES AND TURN OUT SO **MANY** CARTOONS. THE TRUTH IS, WE DON'T.

SOMETIMES RICO BECOMES TOO OVER-WORKED AND EXHAUSTED TO EVEN HOLD A DRAWING PEN!

BUT DO WE WORRY? ...NO! WE JUST GO HOME.

Our most embarrassing cartoons

In our first year of publication, the *Weekly Mail* held a reader survey to determine which features of the newspaper were the most popular. Being young and insecure, we thought we'd create a 'humorous' cartoon — and try to influence the voting at the same time. You have to get up *pretty early in the morning* to outsmart us, hey? An ingenious plan, right? Cringe. Cringe. Cringe. Cringe.

Our first Madam & Eve book had just been released, and naturally we wanted it to be a huge success. So we came up with a brilliant idea — to do a cartoon *and* sneakily advertise the book at the same time! Smart, hey? A few months later, we were so ashamed that we vowed never to print this cartoon again. Until now. We're sorry, OK? Incidentally, our first book became a big success, but we doubt this cartoon had anything to do with it.

We generally don't feel that we've done many cartoons which are in poor taste. But there are exceptions. In this cartoon, Madam paints her face with shoe polish so she can experience what it's like to be a black woman in South Africa. Even though our satirical target was phoney white liberals, and even though we made Madam the butt of the joke, we still cringe when we read this.

30 David vs. Goliath

One day in 1996 we began getting phone calls. People were congratulating us on our television advert. The advert with all our cartoon characters.

There was only one problem: we had no idea what they were talking about.

We all stayed home that night to watch television, remote-control surfing between the three SABC channels. Finally, we saw it.

It was an advert that attempted to convince small businesses to spend their money advertising on television. They may have used live actors instead of animated cartoons, but there, unmistakably, in our opinion, were our characters: Madam. Eve. Mother Anderson. And even (gasp) Mother Anderson's favourite nemesis — the Mielie Lady.

What's more, someone had gone to great lengths to capture the detail of our characters: the unique hairstyles, the large earrings ... even the pearls that Madam and Mother Anderson always wear.

And, to our minds, they had also copied key aspects of the relationships between our characters, particularly the unusual and tense relationship between Mother Anderson and the Mielie Lady.

Naturally, we tracked down the advertising agency responsible the next day and called them up. Their response, to say the least, amazed us.
'What are you talking about?'
'Madam & Eve — no way!'
'It's pure coincidence!'

We were angry, so we consulted our attorneys. Some of the best lawyers in Johannesburg thought we had a strong case, but were we prepared to 'take on' the SABC? Three cartoonists against a huge government institution.

In more than two dozen cartoon strips, the Mielie Lady tried ingenious ways of trying to get into Madam & Eve's home, mainly to get at Mother Anderson. We ran this particular strip just a few months before the TV ad came out. In the TV ad, a Mielie Lady appears on TV — to the obvious anger of the old lady character. Coincidence? You be the judge.

A frame grabbed electronically from the notorious TV advertisement (reproduced here in black and white) and a cartoon panel showing our characters watching TV together, which was published before the TV ad came out. Spot any similarities in their looks, hairstyles, pearls etc, or in the order in which the characters sit on the couch? No? Sure? Well, you're in good company. Neither did the judge.

David vs. Goliath? Were we crazy enough? Sure we were. These were our characters — we felt we had a responsibility to protect them.

And so we proceeded with our lawsuit. All we wanted was for them to stop showing the advert on television, and we brought an urgent application to stop its broadcasting. We finally got our day in court. And we lost. The magistrate ruled that the characters in the TV commercial bore insufficient resemblance to Madam & Eve for our copyright to have been infringed.

We lost the case with costs — and the SABC had spent over R100 000 of taxpayers' money defending the action. It was like taking a test in school and thinking you got an 'A' when suddenly the teacher hands you an 'F'. It's not a great feeling.

Many people, including prominent legal personalities, called us to express their amazement that we hadn't won. An appeal was the obvious way to go. But litigation, even when you are convinced of the righteousness of your case, is expensive. Very expensive. So we decided not to appeal, but rather to pursue other, cheaper, strategies.

Did we do the right thing? Who knows? But we learned a valuable lesson. When we figure out what it is, we'll let you know.

31 Life imitates art

When the local government elections took place in 1995 we decided to let a few Madam & Eve characters stand for office. With more than 10 000 candidates across the country it seemed like everyone was standing anyway. Eve experienced some early canvassing realities. And the Mielie Lady also had to deal with some hostile constituents.

The old cliché, 'truth is often stranger than fiction', is especially true in South Africa. This story imitated aspects of the Madam & Eve cartoon strip. As the press clip puts it: 'A popular comic strip has come to life as the quiet Eastern Cape hamlet of Morgan Bay gears itself up for the elections. The only two women standing for the local government elections, Pebs Saunders and Ntombizodwa Nonqayi, know each other well — Saunders employs Nonqayi as a domestic worker.'

We were amazed at this story — and by the references to our cartoon strip. But we were heartened too. The gist of the situation said so much about that which is weird and wonderful in the New South Africa.

A few weeks afterwards, a second article appeared announcing the election results. This time the undercurrent of the story was not quite as pleasant. Nonqayi, the domestic worker, had lost, and the election seemed to have divided the town along racial lines. Reality is never as much fun as a cartoon strip.

But, as the second story concludes, even though Nonqayi lost, and had to go back to working as an 'Eve', her party, the ANC, won the region, so the political power balance was fairly even in the end. Let nobody tell you we don't live in an interesting country.

Maid vs madam in Morgan Bay

Bronwen Roberts

A POPULAR comic strip has come to life as the quiet Eastern Cape hamlet of Morgan Bay gears itself up for the elections.

The only two women standing for the local government elections, Pebs Saunders and Ntombizodwa Nonqayi, know one another well — Saunders employs Nonqayi as a domestic worker.

And, in a scenario that seems straight out of the *Madam and Eve* cartoon series, Nonqayi is standing for election against her employer.

"It is a bit of a giggle," smiles Saunders, who is from the independent Kei Mouth/Morgan Bay Ratepayers' Association.

She seems to feel a bit uncomfortable about the situation, but says Ivy — as she calls Nonqayi — "has every democratic right to stand for elections".

"I think it is the ANC ...

... want to make too much of the whole thing."

About 500 metres down the road from Saunders' luxury home, which ... estate agency office ... can't find" and ...

... rondavels and shacks in a village that climbs an uneven and rocky slope.

Nonqayi says the village is called "Lokohlo", which means "the place ...

... and view of the sea and the Ntshala River lagoon that visitors associate with Morgan Bay.

The village is very traditional and so is Nonqayi, standing among half-naked children and wearing a doek and German print dress, her face lightly whitened.

One of her election hopes is to get a better location for her village, where people can build enough homes so that several families do not have to live together.

Other promises include those the ANC clings to — water, electricity, a sewerage system.

Nonqayi is excited about the elections; Saunders, an experienced councillor, is a bit more fierce. "Morgan Bay is my baby," she says.

The two don't discuss the election much. Nonqayi arrives at work and starts her morning's chores, while Saunders takes off in her bakkie to do ...

The two articles, from the *Mail & Guardian* and *The Star* respectively, report on the real-life replay of one of our cartoon strip situations.

'Madam' won, and it's back to the kitchen for 'Eve'

Morgan Bay - Madam has won — and it's back to scrubbing the floors for Morgan Bay domestic servant Ntombizodwa Nonqayi.

It was a real-life replay of the popular all-South African comic-strip *Madam and Eve* which pokes fun at the relationship between white women and their domestic servants.

In Morgan Bay, Nonqayi and her "madam", Pebs Saunders, both contested the elections.

But Saunders yesterday convincingly beat the woman she calls "Ivy", by 192 votes. She scored 237 votes to Nonqayi's 65.

... and was unav... ...

... comment yesterday.

She had reportedly gone to her humble home in Lokohlo village, which is a scraggly collection of huts and shacks, without phones, on the hilltop above her madam's home.

In sharp contrast, Saunders has her home and estate agency in Morgan Bay itself, an idyllic seaside village perched on the edge of a vast beach and framed by a series of spectacular basalt cliffs.

However, another losing candidate in the ward, Laurence Xolo, said he was with Nonqayi ... the results ...

... ounced. "She was very angry about losing."

Xolo, the bartender at the festive Morgan Bay Hotel, said Nonqayi had badly wanted to defeat her employer at the ballot box.

He claimed that in the build-up to the election whites in Morgan Bay had joked cruelly about "Eve wanting to get madam to wash her floors and cook for her if she won".

However, one white woman in town explained yesterday: "Look, she (Mrs Non... ... very une... ...

The winning "madam", Mrs Saunders, was gracious about her win.

She said yesterday: "I've got a lot of work to do and we'll get along together ... She's a very nice person and if she's got an interest (in politics) she must carry on. She's got lots to learn. I probably have too!

But it wasn't all bad news for Nonqayi. Her party, the ANC, won four out of six seats in the Morgan Bay/Kei Mouth area.

That means Eve's party will rule over Democratic Party councillors F G Nisho... ...

Education with a punchline

We've given hundreds of publishers, schools, corporations, NGOs and other organisations permission to reproduce Madam & Eve cartoons. Sometimes, such as when the publications are for profit, we charge an appropriate fee, but usually we're just happy to see our cartoons being put to good use.

We've also seen Madam & Eve used in examination papers in almost every high school subject at one time or another. If any teachers are reading this, and are wondering if you need our permission to copy our cartoons, the answer is no, you don't. As long as you use just a few strips, and only for legitimate education purposes such as illustrating lessons, or brightening up exams and tests, that's OK by us. In fact, we'd love you to use Madam & Eve to make education more fun.

This particular example comes from *Business English*, published by Heinemann. We even took the test ourselves. We failed.

Cartoon A: MADAM & EVE

Cartoon B: MADAM & EVE

(Cartoons A and B published with permission of the *Rapid Phase Entertainment Group*)

Comprehension

Study cartoons A and B carefully a number of times and then answer the questions that follow, using your own words:

Cartoon A
1. What service is Eve offering?
2. Rewrite '20 bucks' in more formal language.
3. Why is Eve's employer upset with her?
4. Explain the metaphor used in 'hop on the gravy train'.
5. What tells us that Mrs Anderson is angry in frame 3?

Surfing the net:
Madam&Eve and the future

A couple of years ago we got a call from the *Weekly Mail and Guardian* who suggested we should get Madam & Eve onto the information super highway as soon as possible.

We told them this would be difficult as Madam hates to drive, except maybe to go shopping.

Then they explained that they meant the Internet and the World Wide Web. Then they explained what those things were.

Great idea, we thought — of course Madam & Eve must have their own web site. So we got busy designing the site, which the *Electronic Mail and Guardian* built for us, and since early 1996, the Madam & Eve homepage (http://www.mg.co.za/mg/) has become a popular attraction for web surfers all over the world.

In fact, we're told that more than 50 000 people now check out the Madam & Eve site each month, and we get a fair amount of e-mail. We love the immediacy of the web — people in Hoboken, New Jersey, or Osaka, Japan, and lots of places we've never heard of, can now read the latest Madam & Eve cartoon every day. What's more they can dash off an e-mail letter to us instantaneously, telling us what they think about the cartoon.

If you enter http://www.mg.co.za/mg/ on your Internet browser, you'll get to this Madam & Eve home page with just a few clicks of your mouse. From this opening page you can call up classic Madam & Eve cartoons, or check out the latest daily and weekly cartoon.

What we're finding is that the Internet is changing the way in which cartoons are delivered to audiences — we have thousands of new readers who have only seen Madam & Eve on a computer screen.

Of course we believe people also like the old fashioned holding-a-book in your hand way of reading cartoons, so we've developed an on-line ordering system for Madam & Eve products on our web site, with many sales to international readers. Just remember, we do it for fun. The money we make has absolutely nothing to do with it.

New sections of the Madam & Eve Homepage are under construction all the time, and a whole lot of new Madam & Eve products are made available through our on-line mail order service as and when they become available.

We even have plans for an interactive Madam & Eve quiz, a downloadable Madam & Eve screen saver, and lots of other fun electronic stuff.

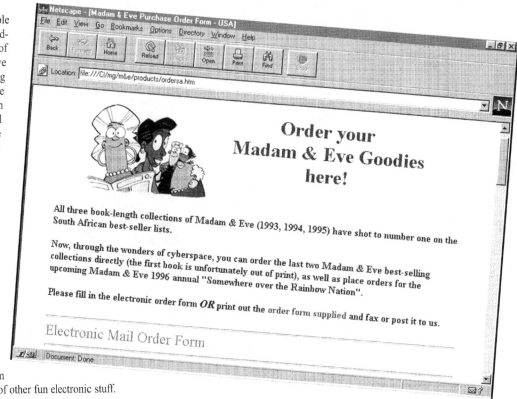

Netscape - [Madam & Eve Purchase Order Form - USA]

File Edit View Go Bookmarks Options Directory Window Help

Location: file:///C|/mg/m&e/products/ordersa.htm

Order your Madam & Eve Goodies here!

All three book-length collections of Madam & Eve (1993, 1994, 1995) have shot to number one on the South African best-seller lists.

Now, through the wonders of cyberspace, you can order the last two Madam & Eve best-selling collections directly (the first book is unfortunately out of print), as well as place orders for the upcoming Madam & Eve 1996 annual "Somewhere over the Rainbow Nation".

Please fill in the electronic order form **OR** print out the order form supplied and fax or post it to us.

Electronic Mail Order Form

Document: Done

Politically incorrect

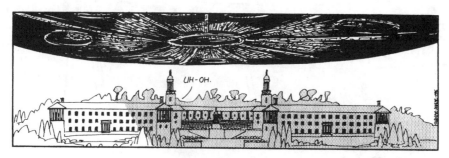

UH-OH.

Even President Nelson Mandela seems to take his appearances in Madam & Eve cartoons with good humour. (We hope so. He's in quite a few.) At the Foreign Correspondents Annual Dinner we were thrilled to be able to present him with a series of original cartoons featuring him. (That's the three of us on the left.)

People often ask us what reaction we get from politicians and celebrities who appear in the cartoon strip. So far, no one has punched any of us in the nose, so we take that as a positive sign. One of our favourite subjects has always been Winnie Madikizela-Mandela. Unfortunately though, she hasn't called or written with her comments. Winnie, if you're reading this, give us a call. We'd love to hear from you.

Minister of Sport, Steve Tshwete, was recently asked in an interview if he could choose to be any fictional character, whom would he choose? He picked Eve. We're thinking of creating a new cartoon, 'Madam & Steve'.

Jacquie Golding-Duffy

MEDIA MAD

Minister of Sport and Recreation STEVE TSHWETE sees himself as Eve in the cartoon strip *Madam and Eve*

Which television programmes do you watch most often and why? News programmes and talk shows. To follow up on international and national news and listen to opinions of ordinary people on television talk shows.
Which book have you recently read that you would recommend? Tolstoy's *War and Peace*.
Which radio stations do you listen to and why? Current Affairs programmes of SAFM as the reports are well researched and provide detailed news.
Do you surf the World Wide Web of the Internet and what do particularly go for? No, I don't surf the Web.
Which is your favourite advertisement and why? The Sanlam advertisement with little kids in a sort of board meeting.
Which newspapers and magazines do you regularly read? *Citizen, Mail & Guardian, Sunday Independent, Sowetan, Enterprise* and various sports magazines.
If you could be any film star or fictional character, who would you be and why? Eve of the *Madam and Eve* cartoon, for her outright, down-to-earth response to racism and her ability to make a fool of the ambitious and highly conceited Madam.

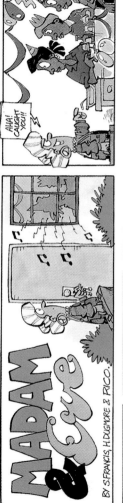

POST CARD

POST CARD

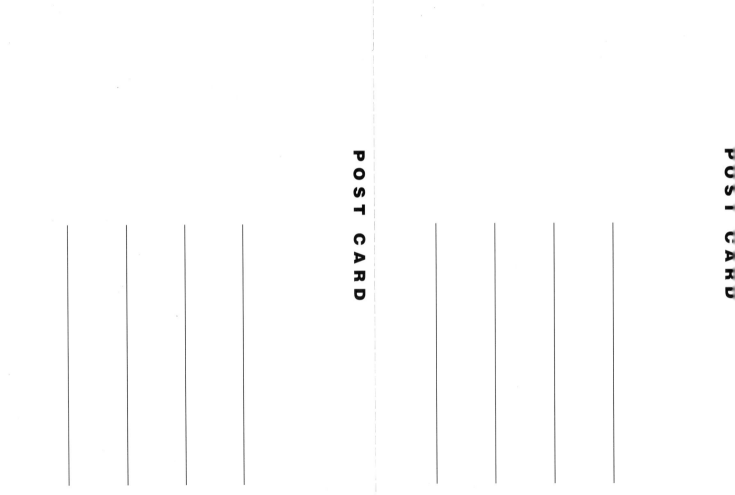

POST CARD

POST CARD